THIS BOOK BELONGS TO :

Emergency Contact Name/Number:

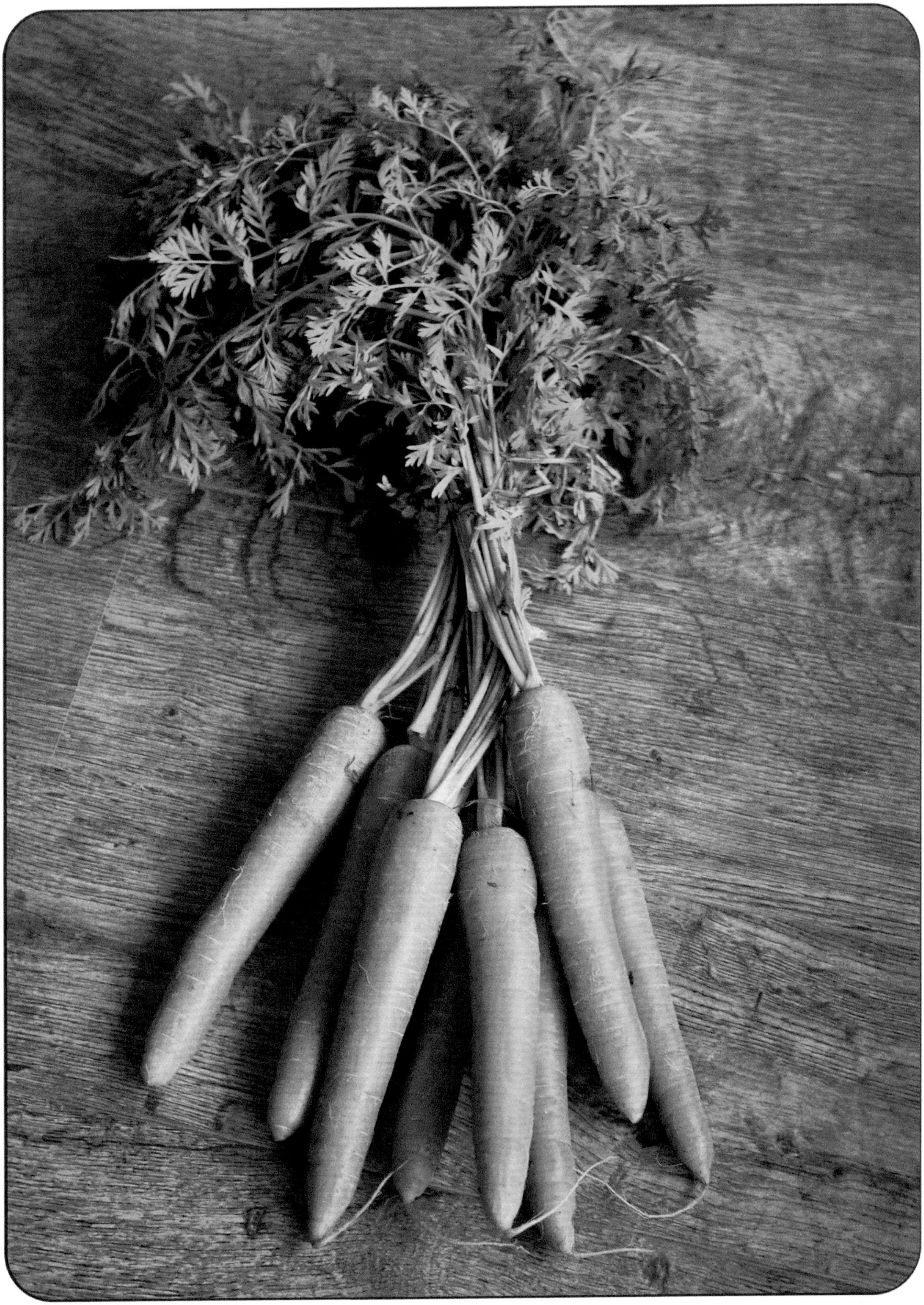

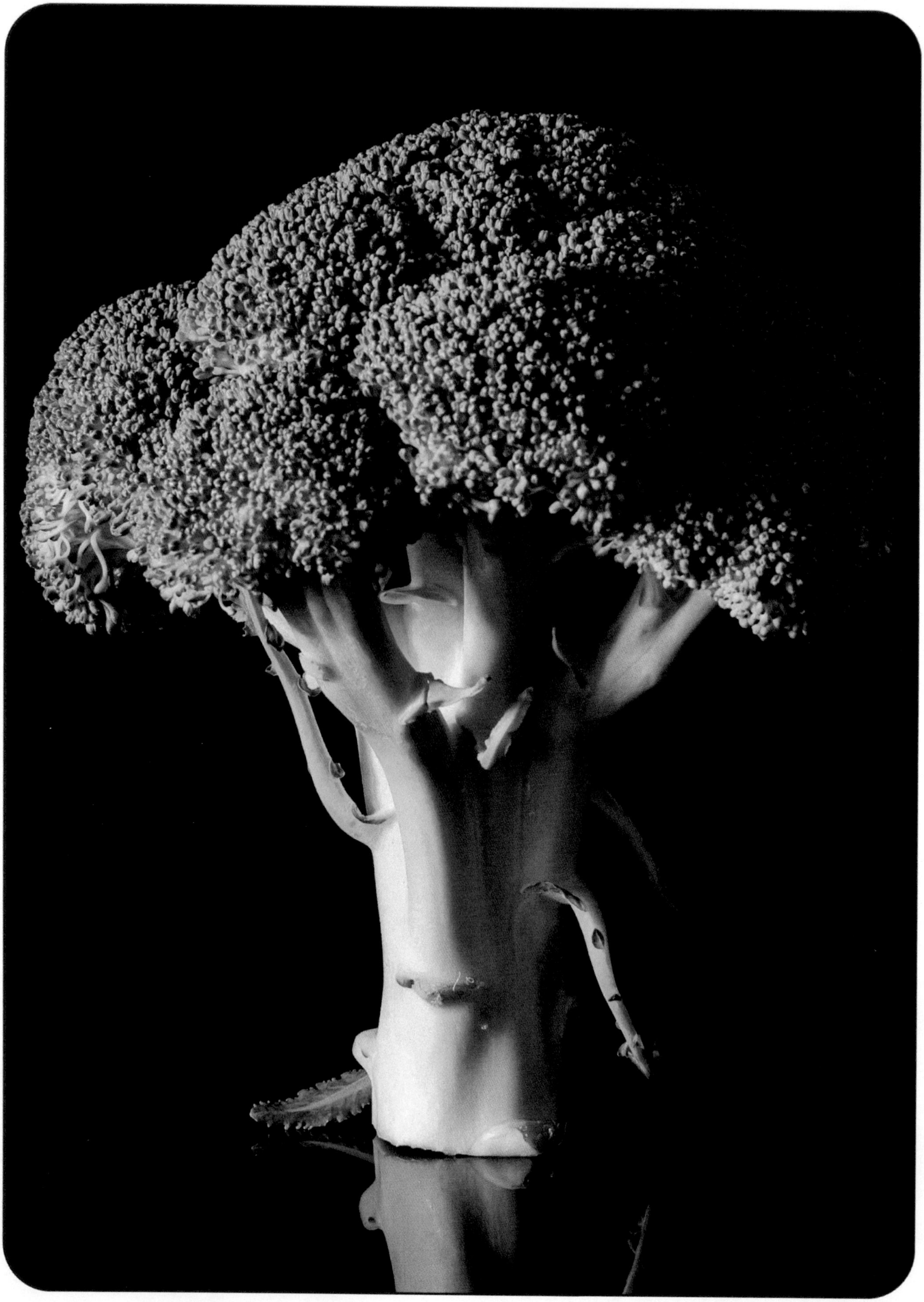

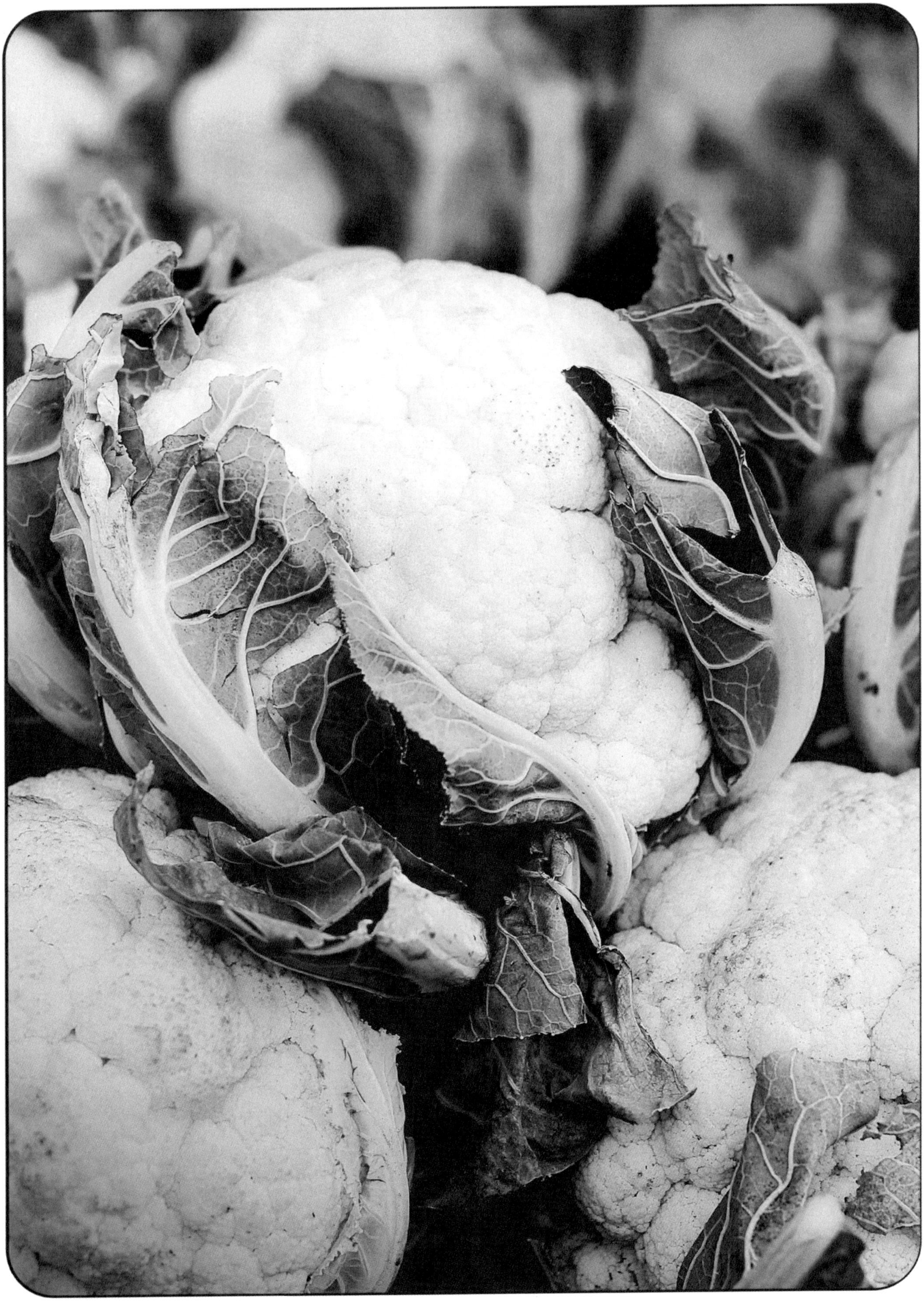

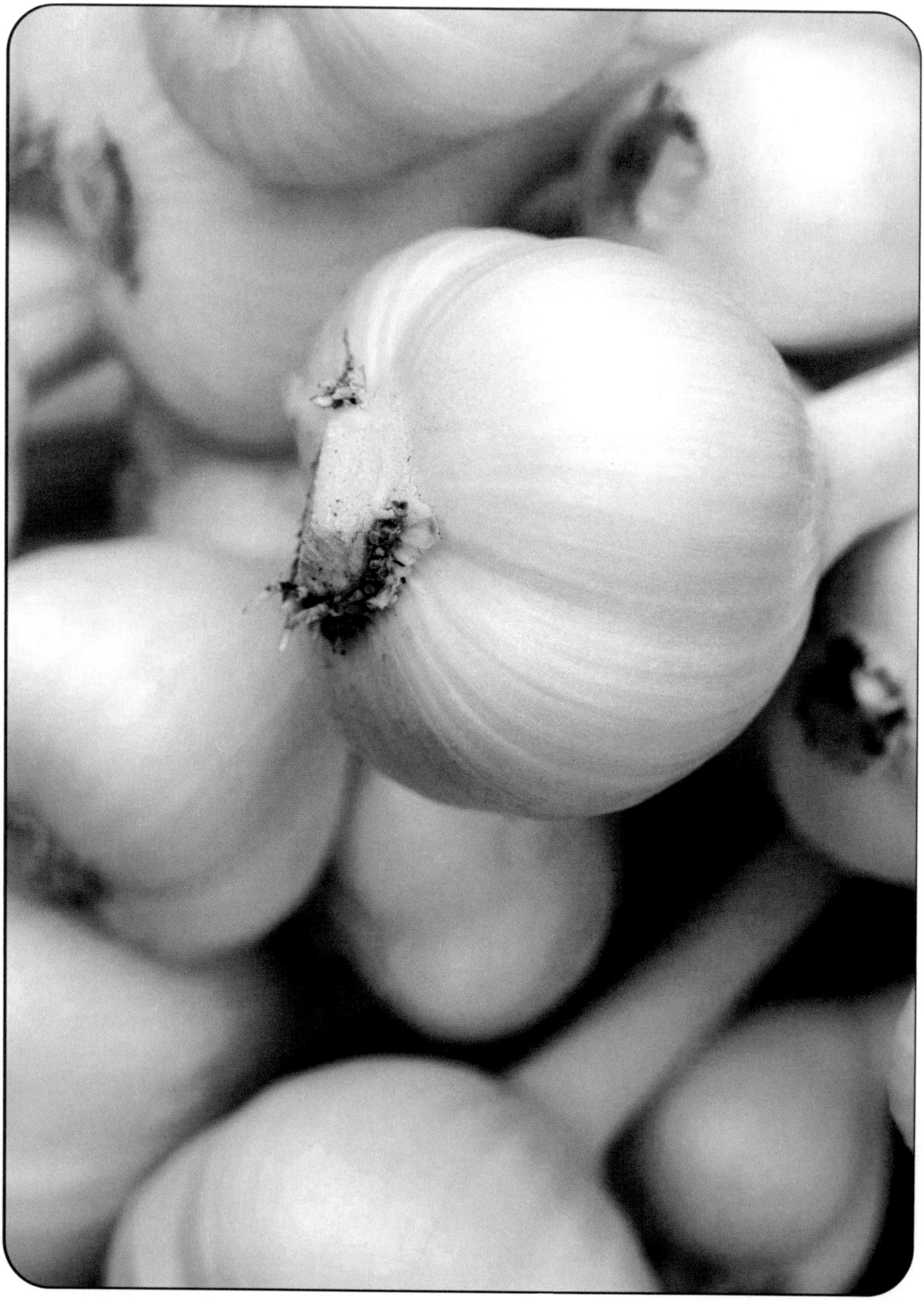

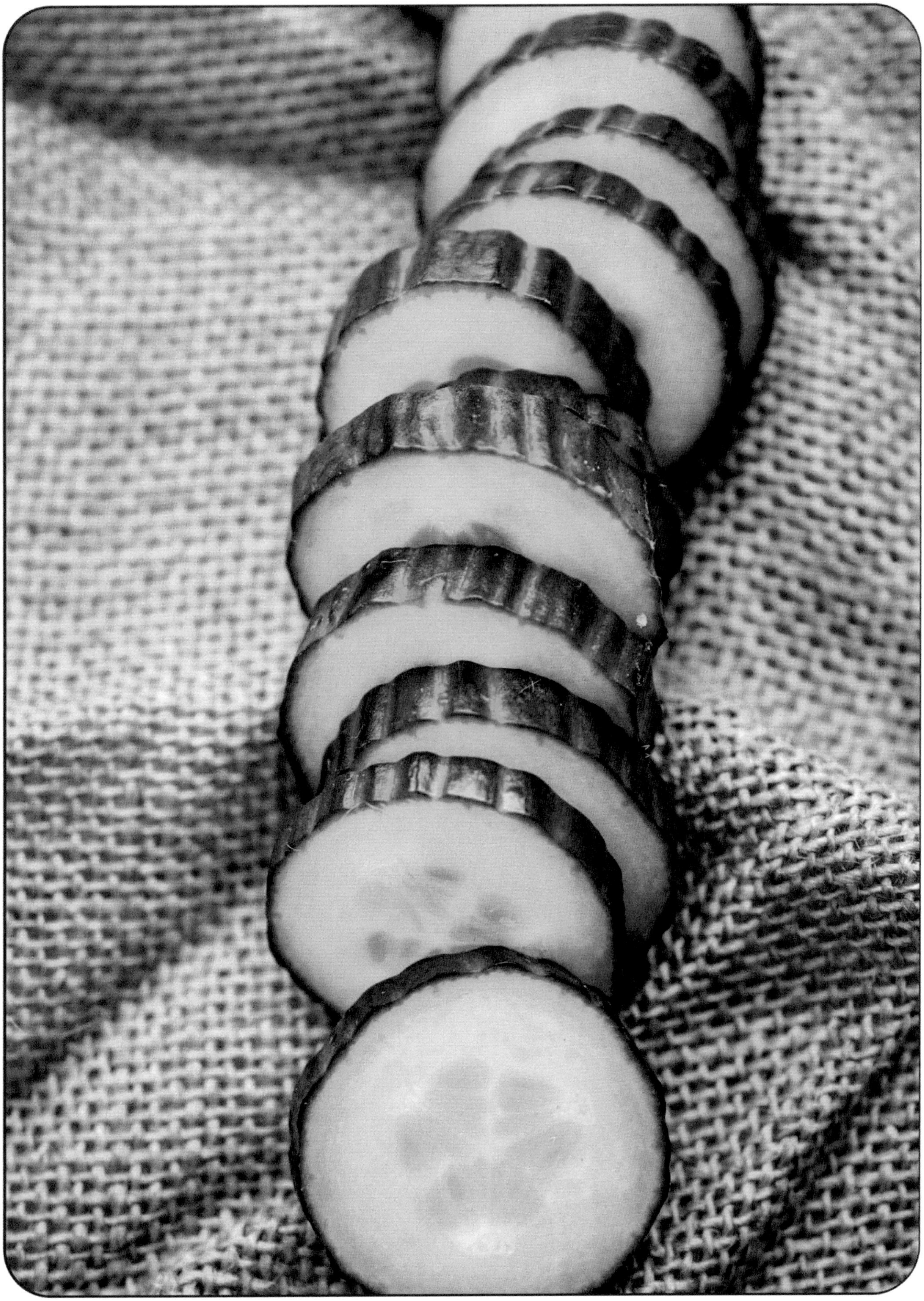

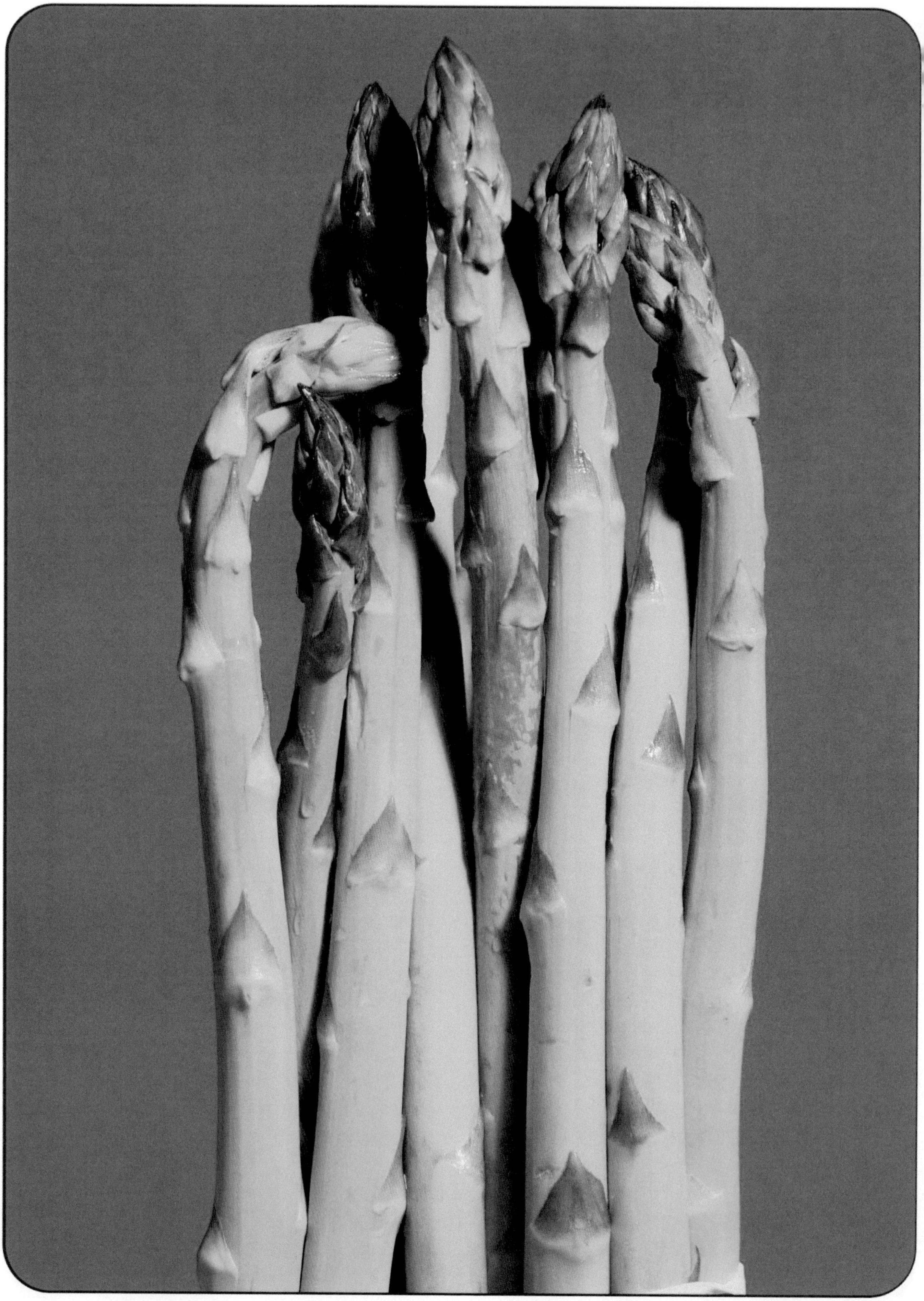

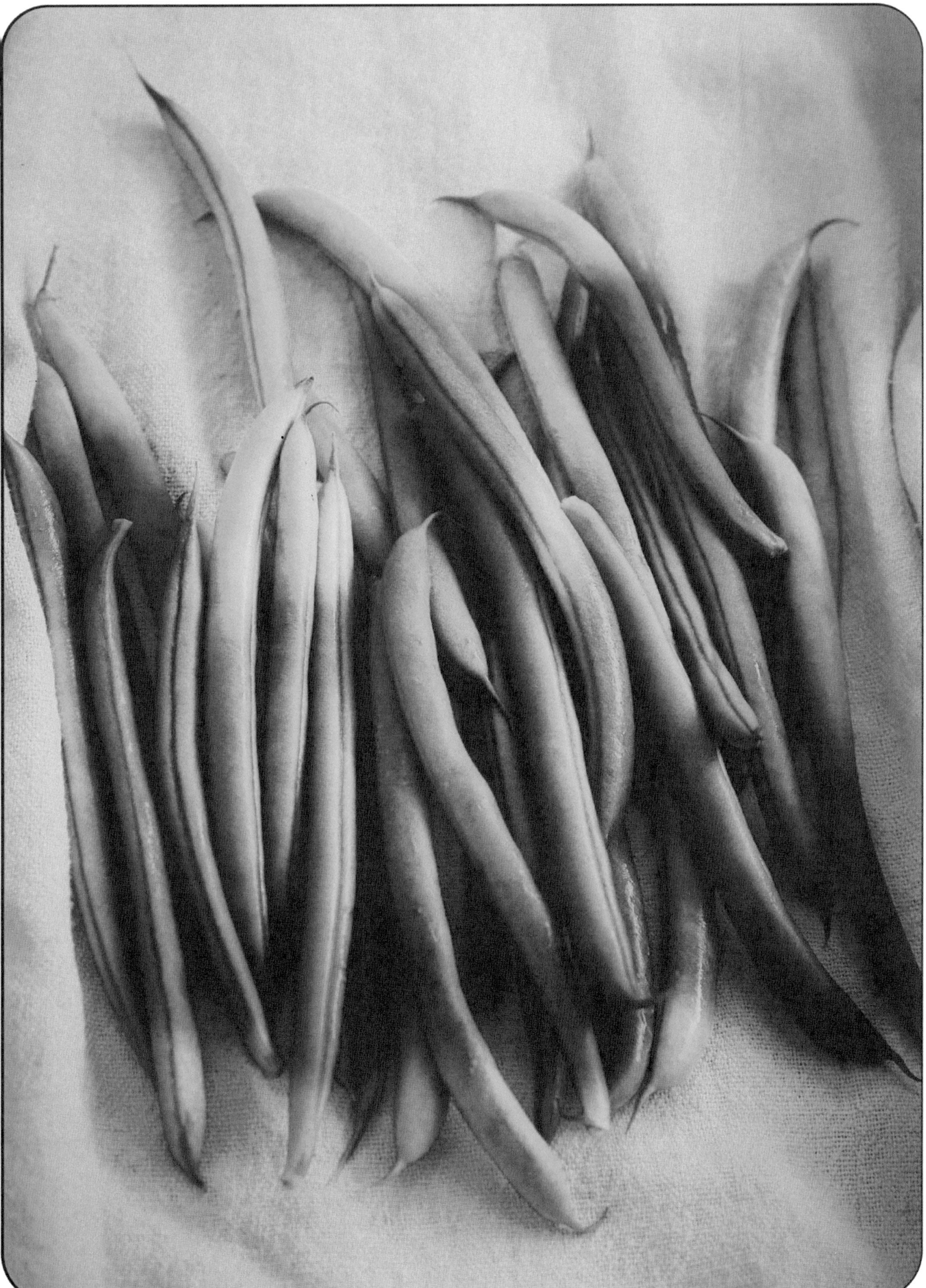

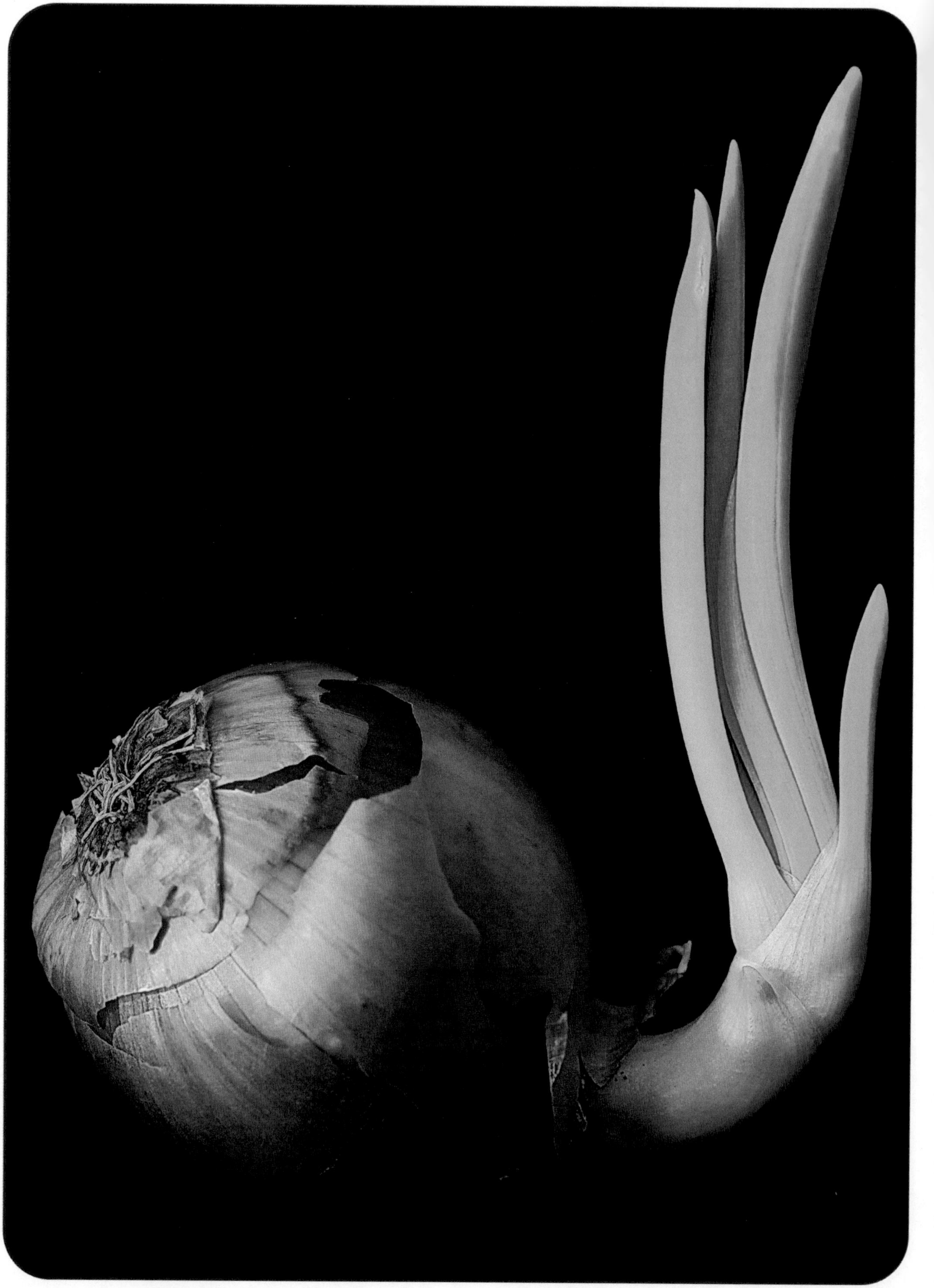

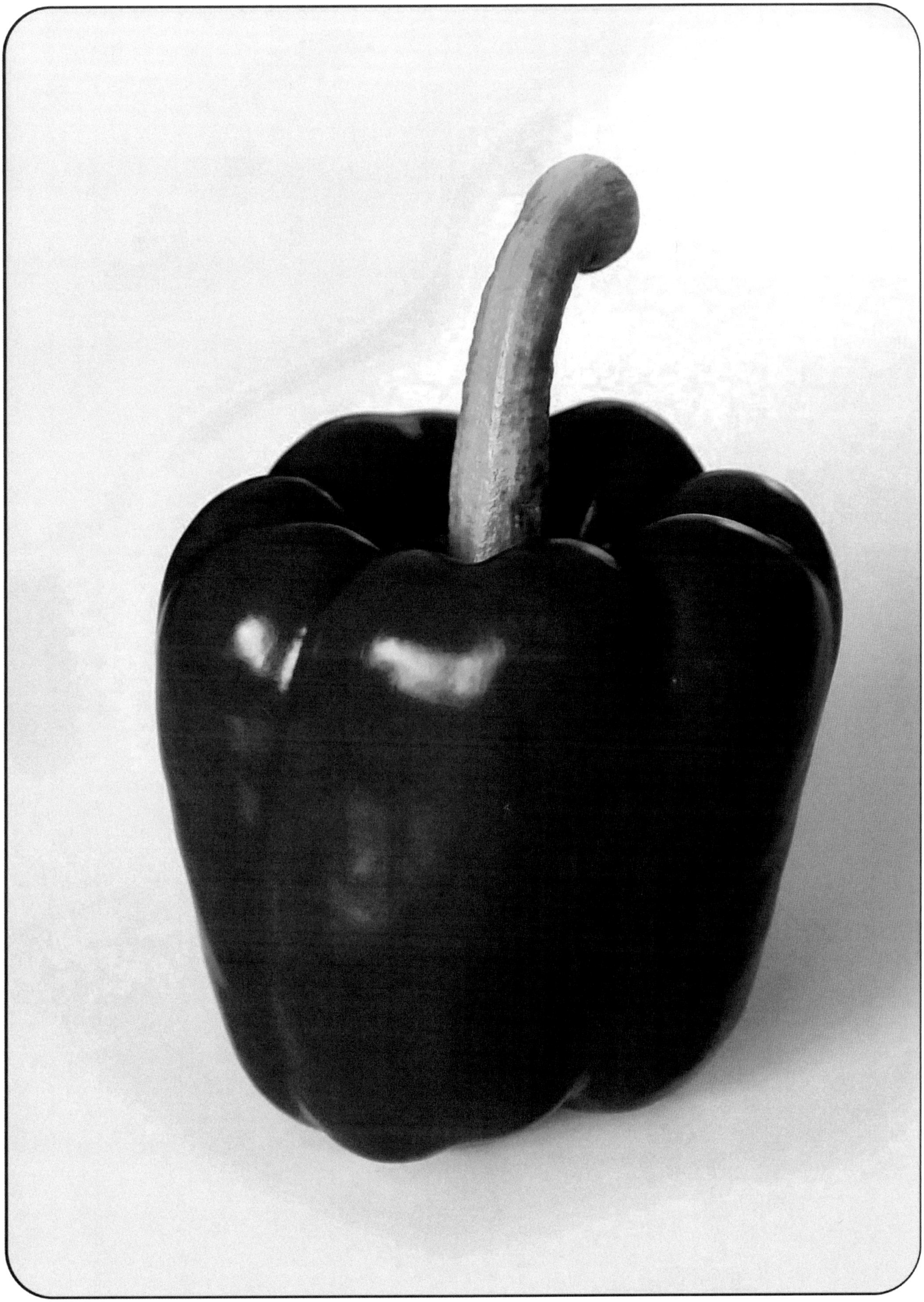

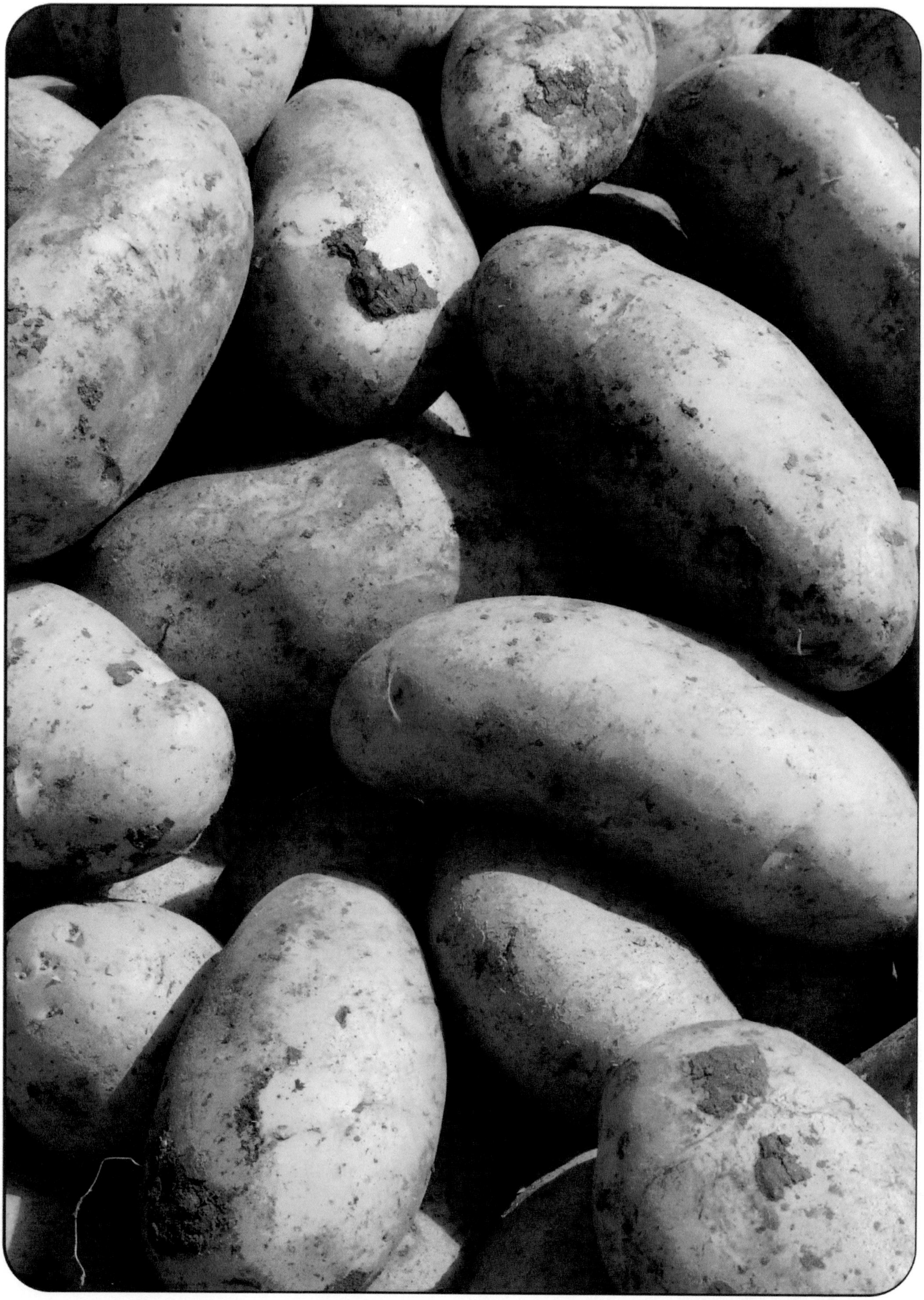

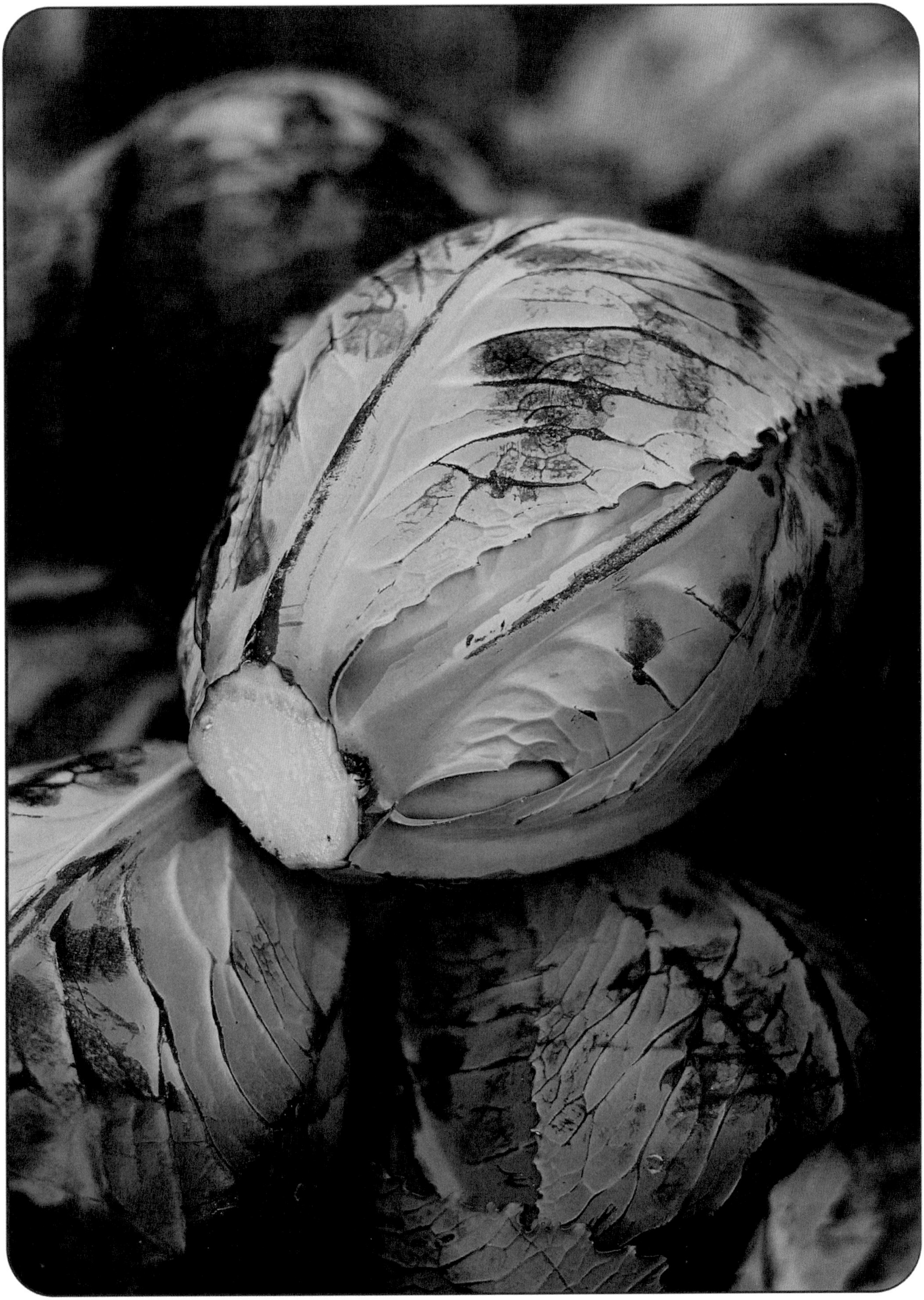

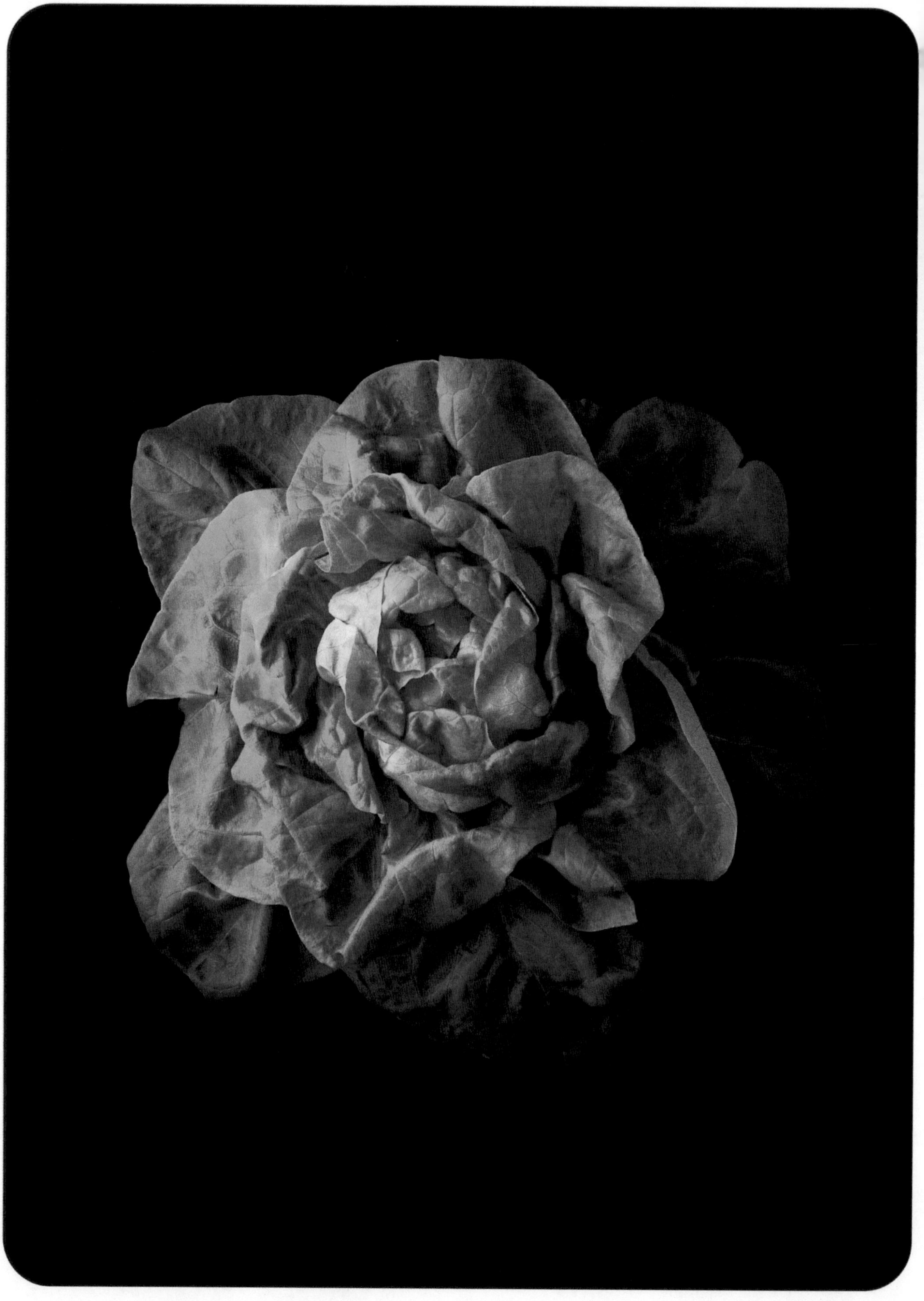

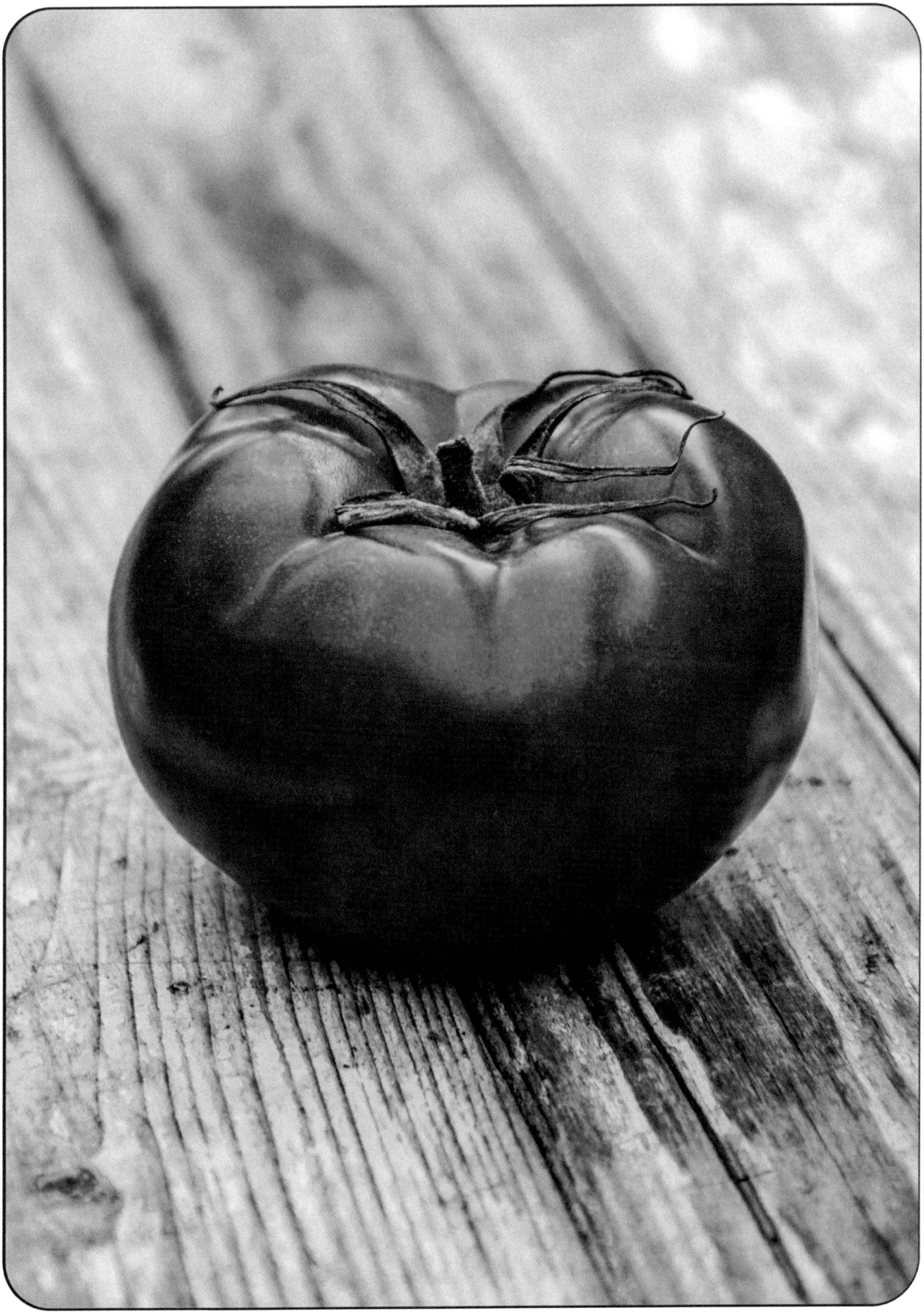

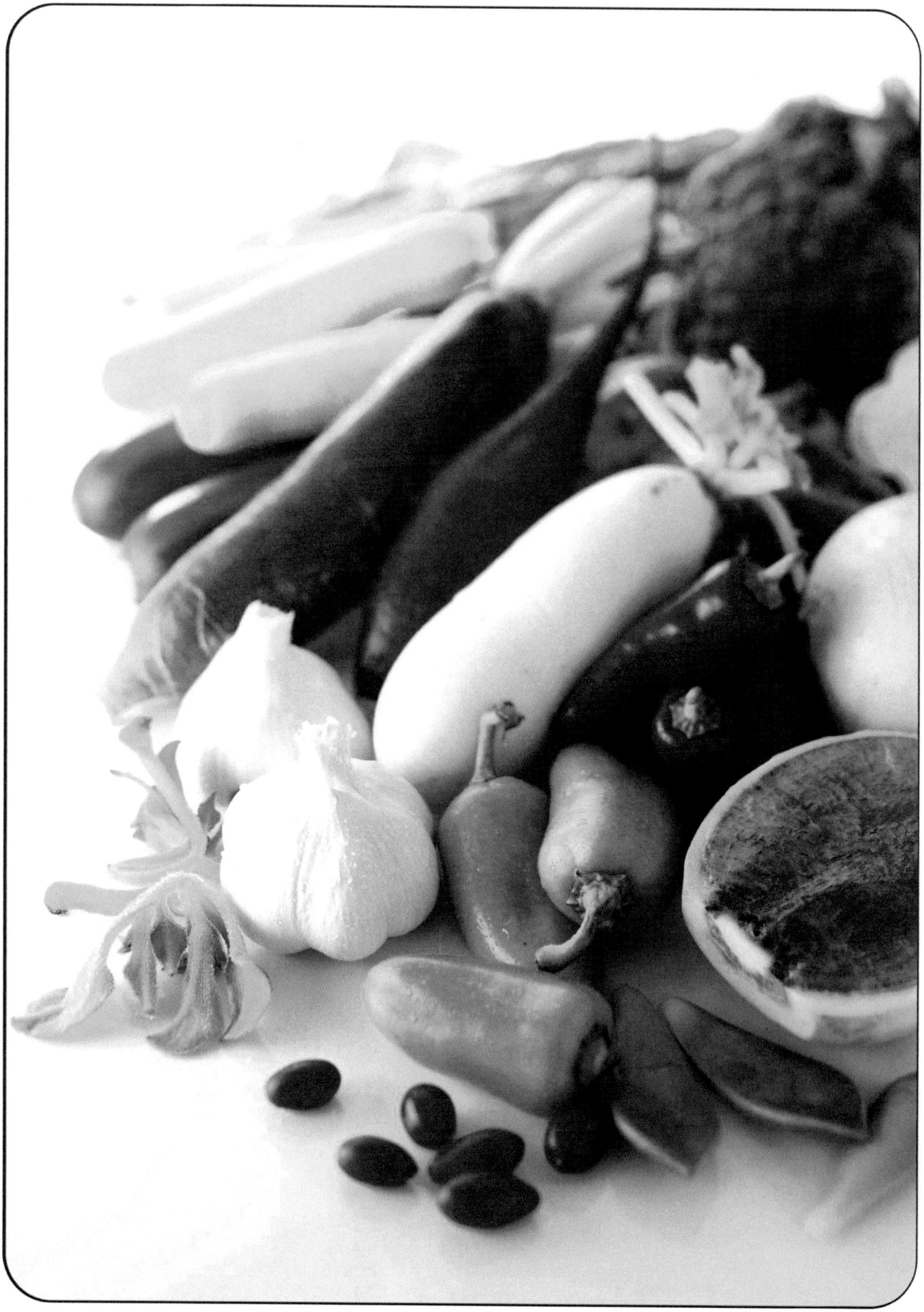

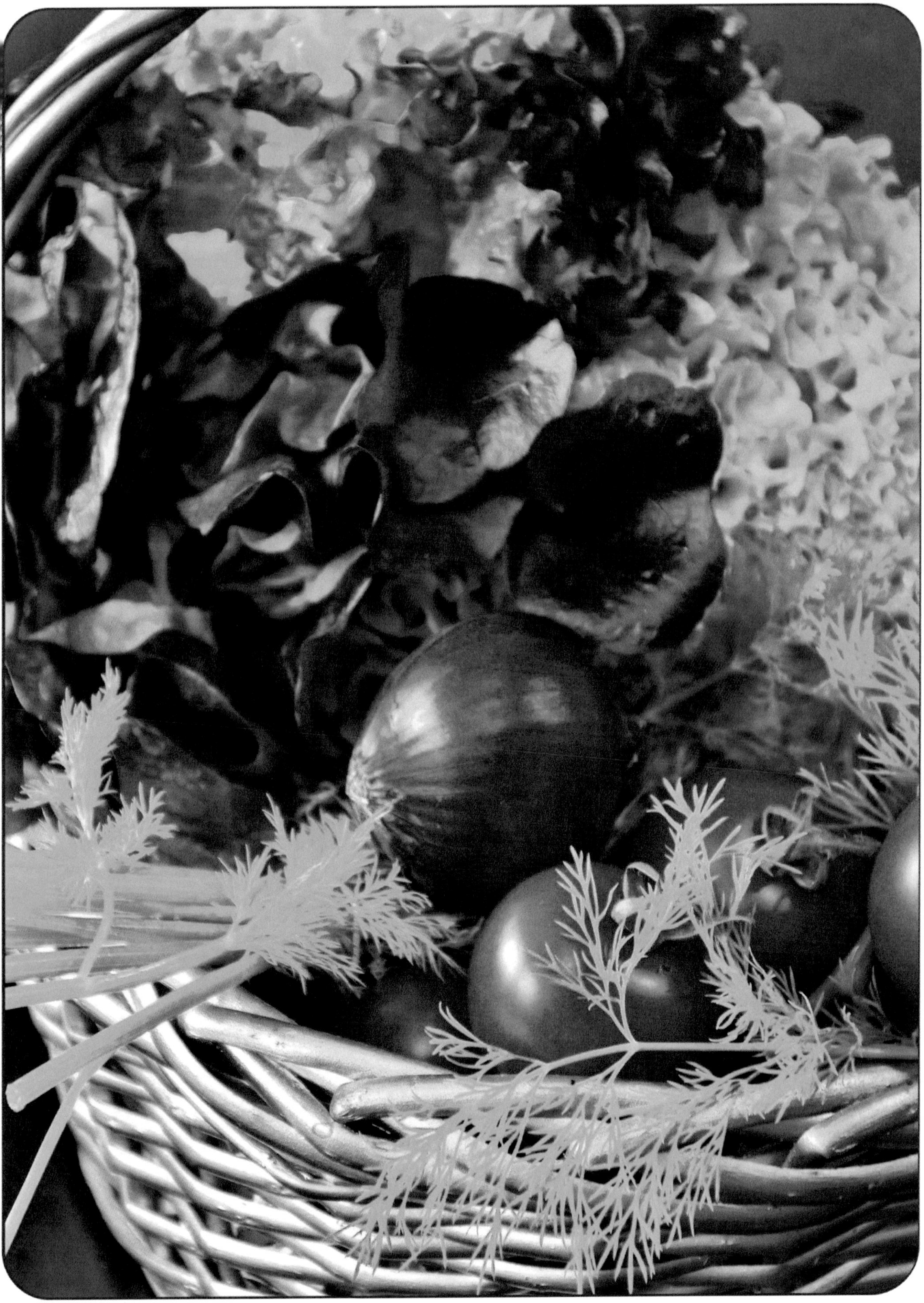

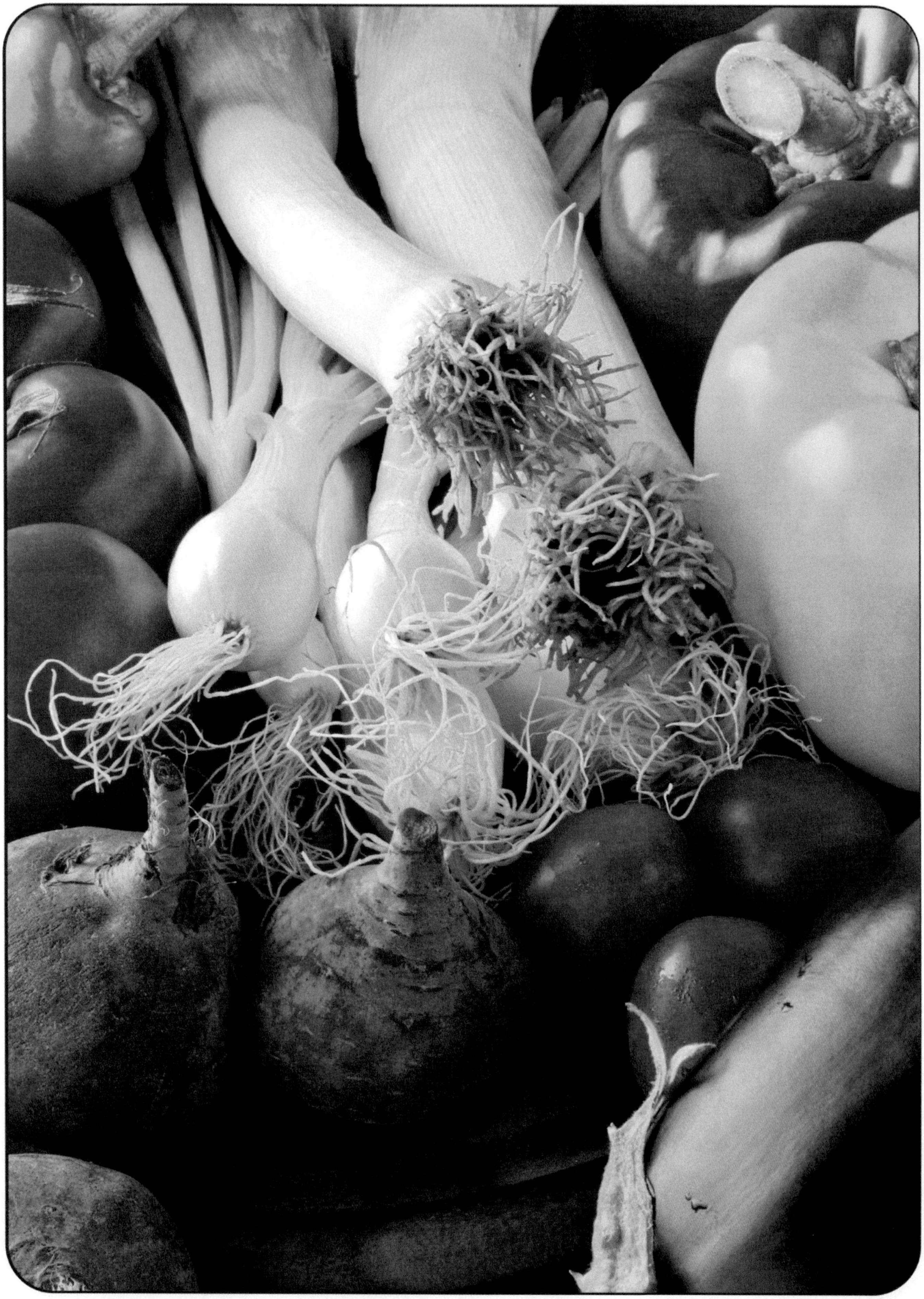

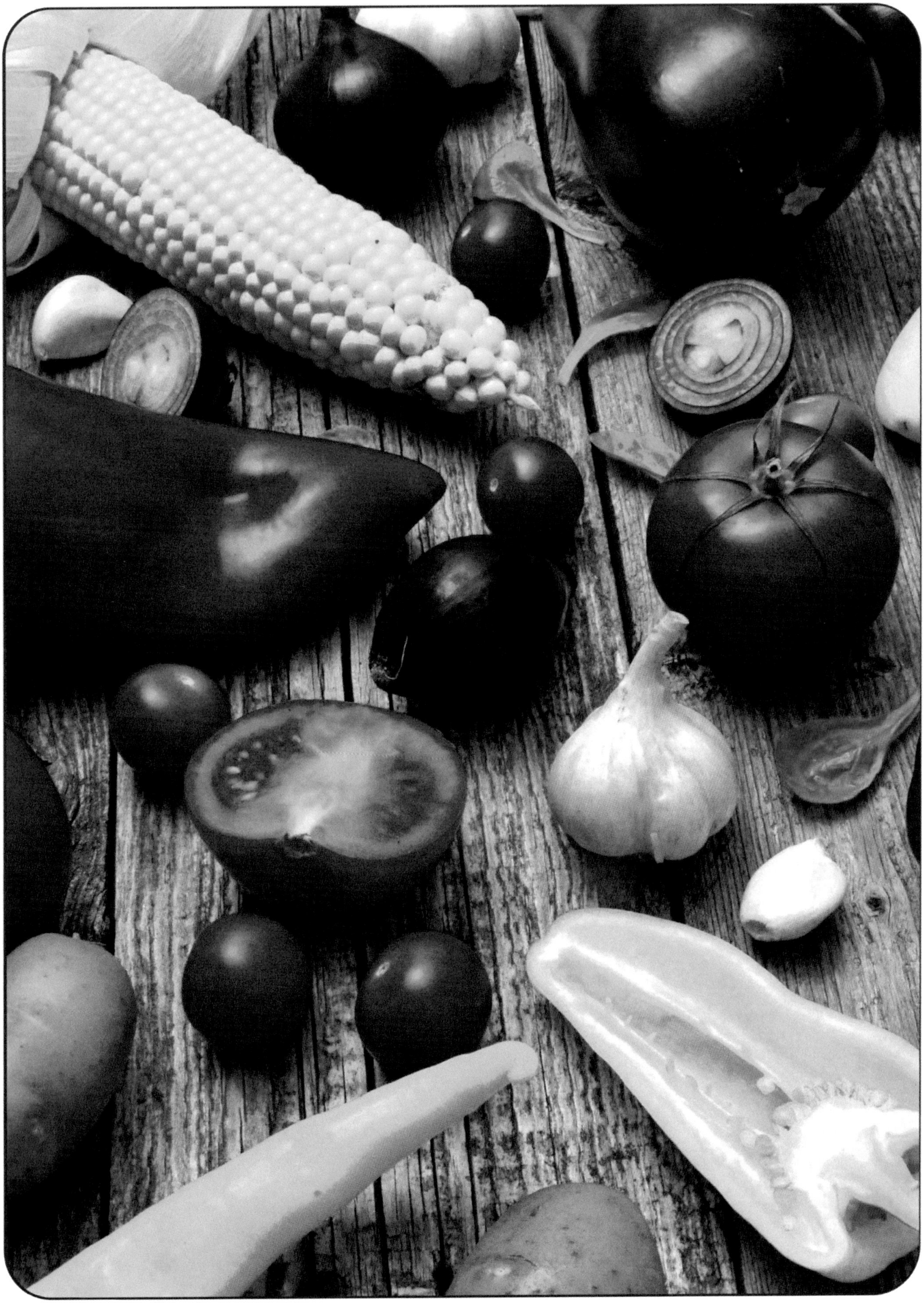

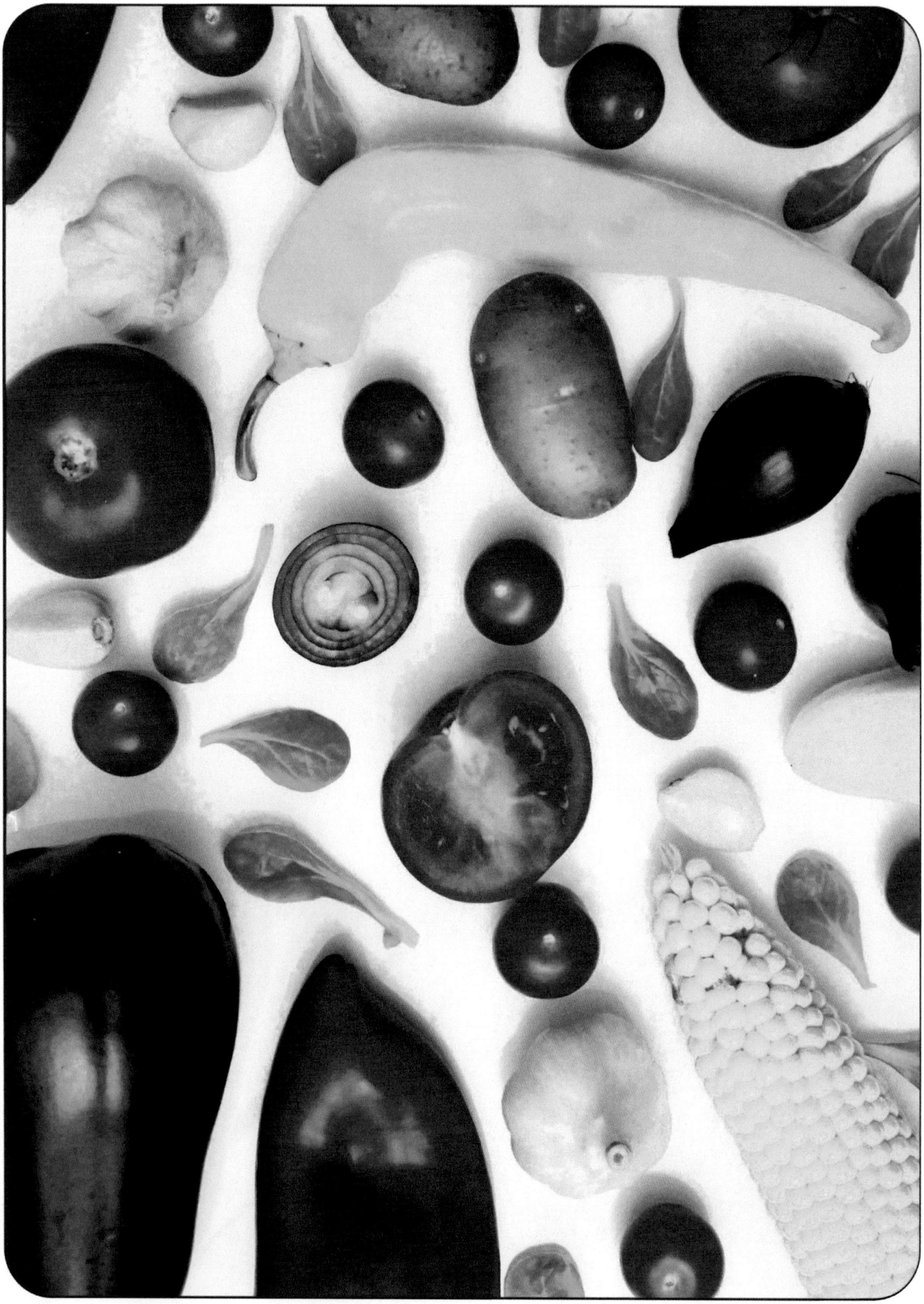

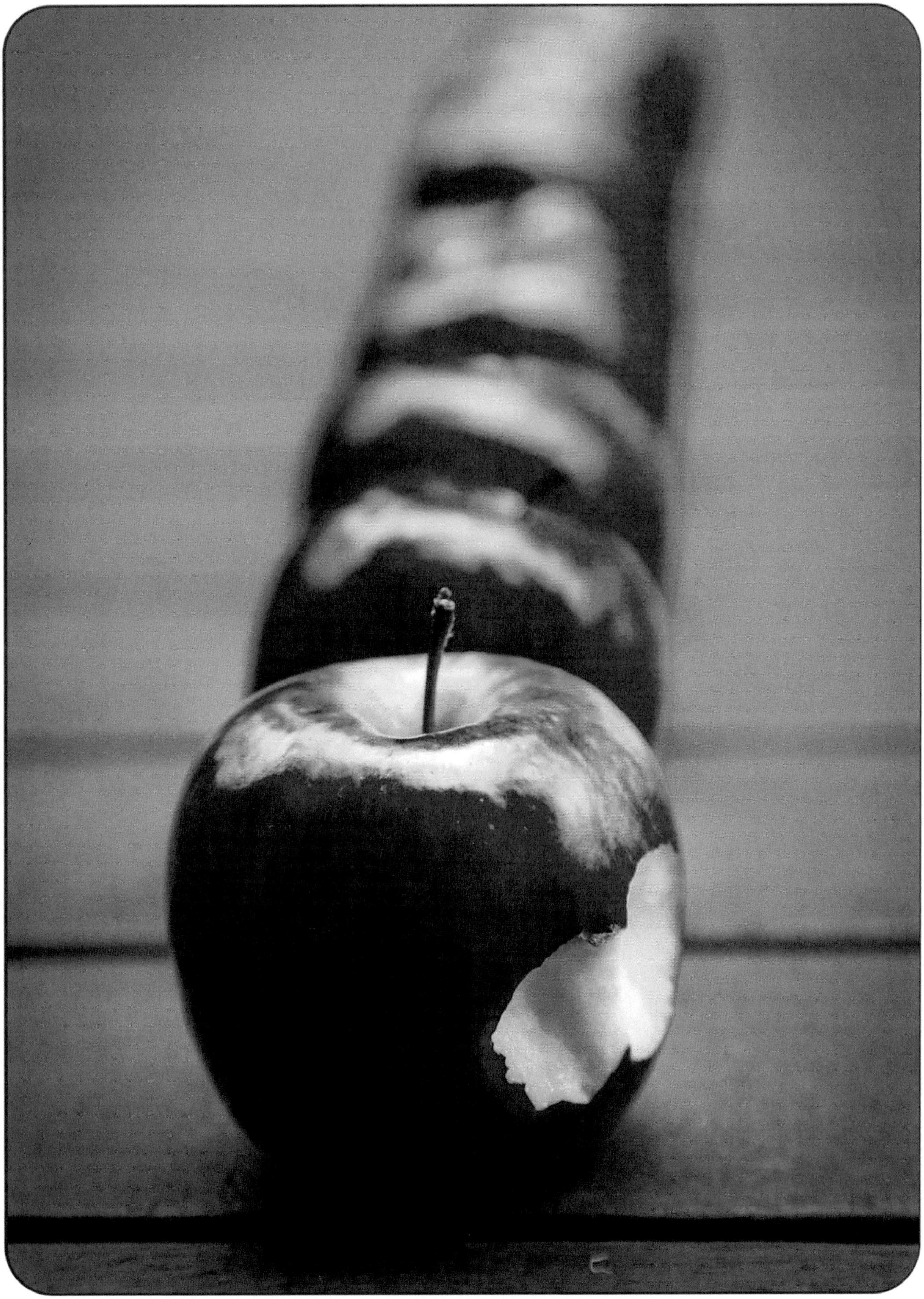

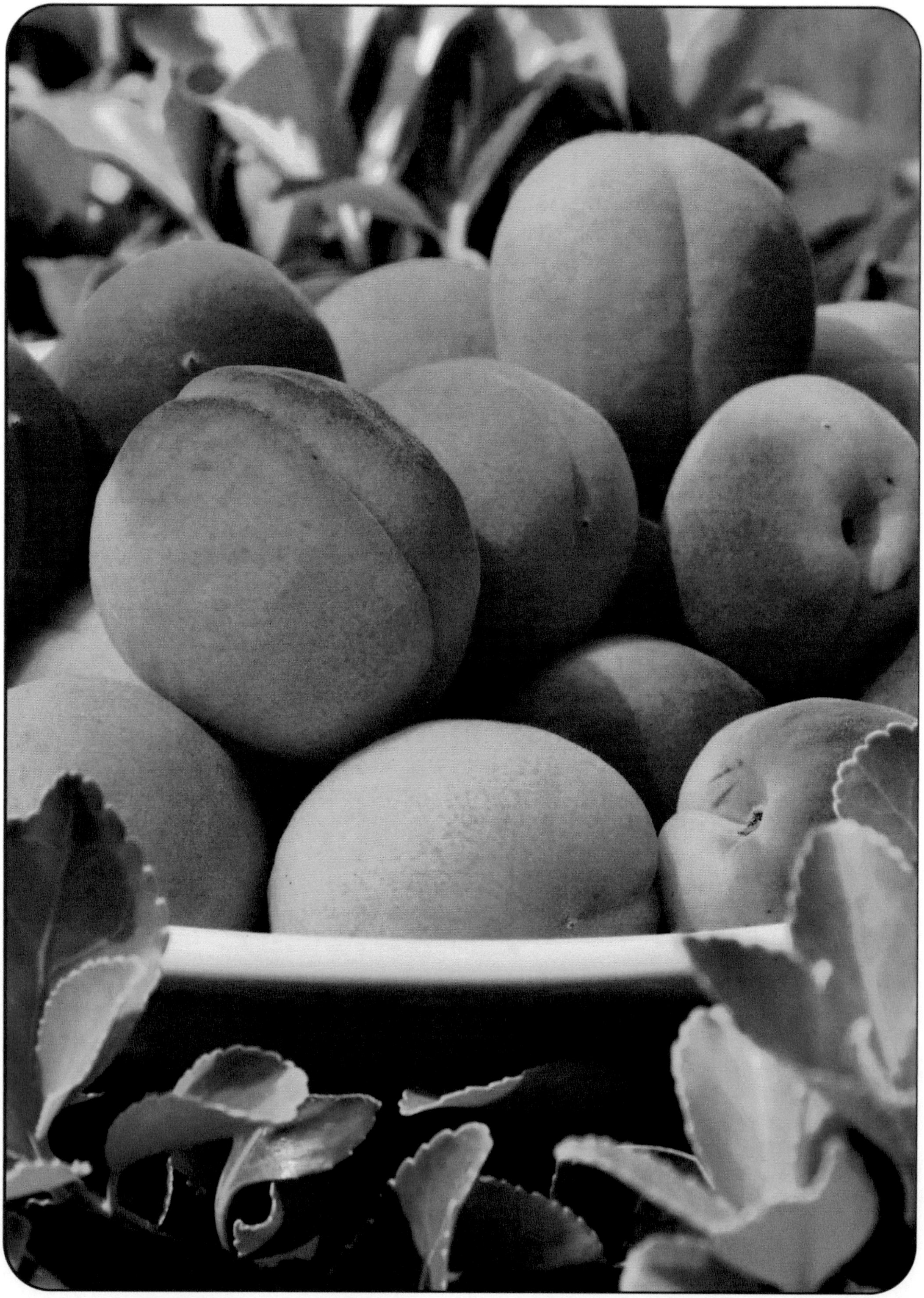

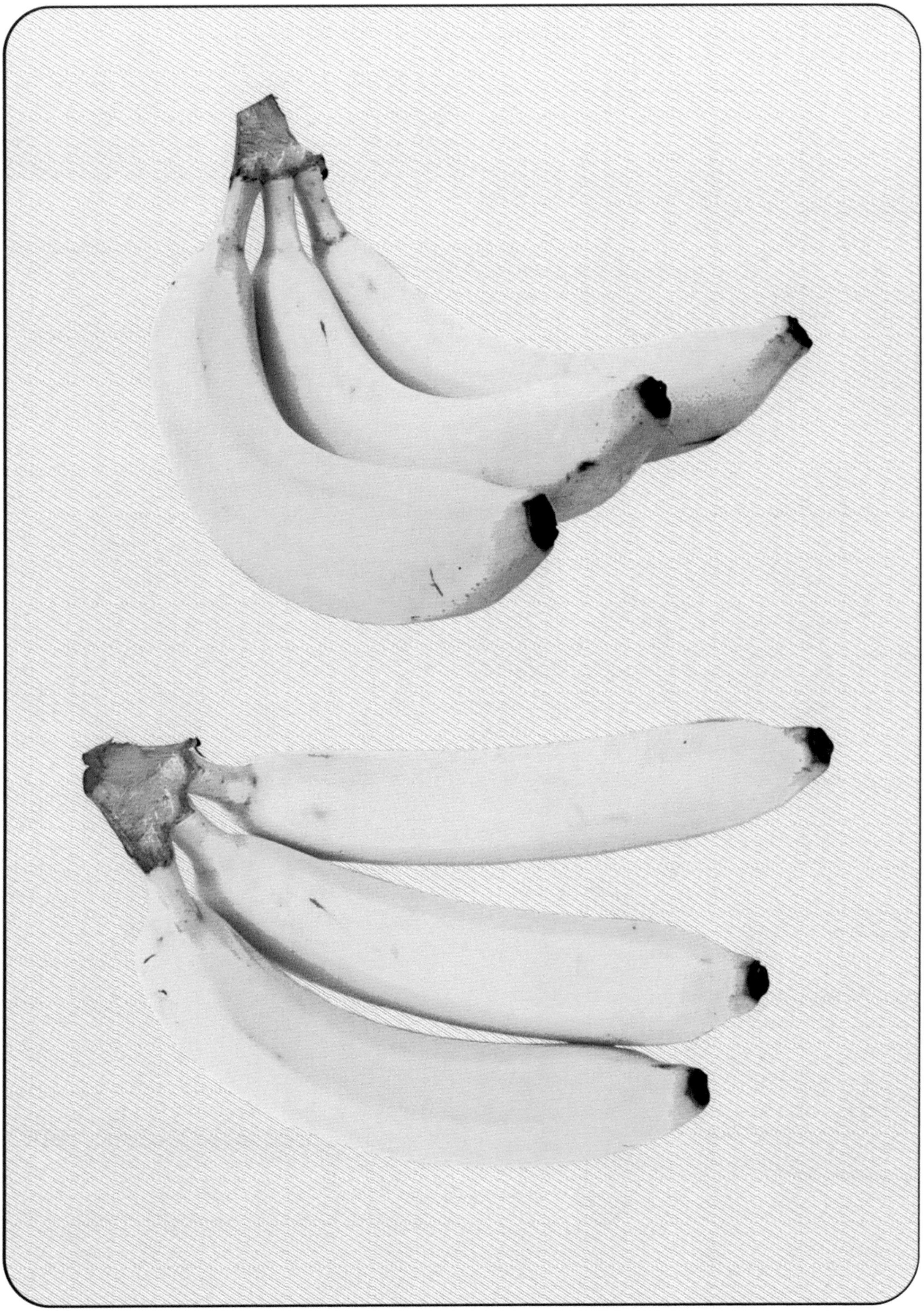

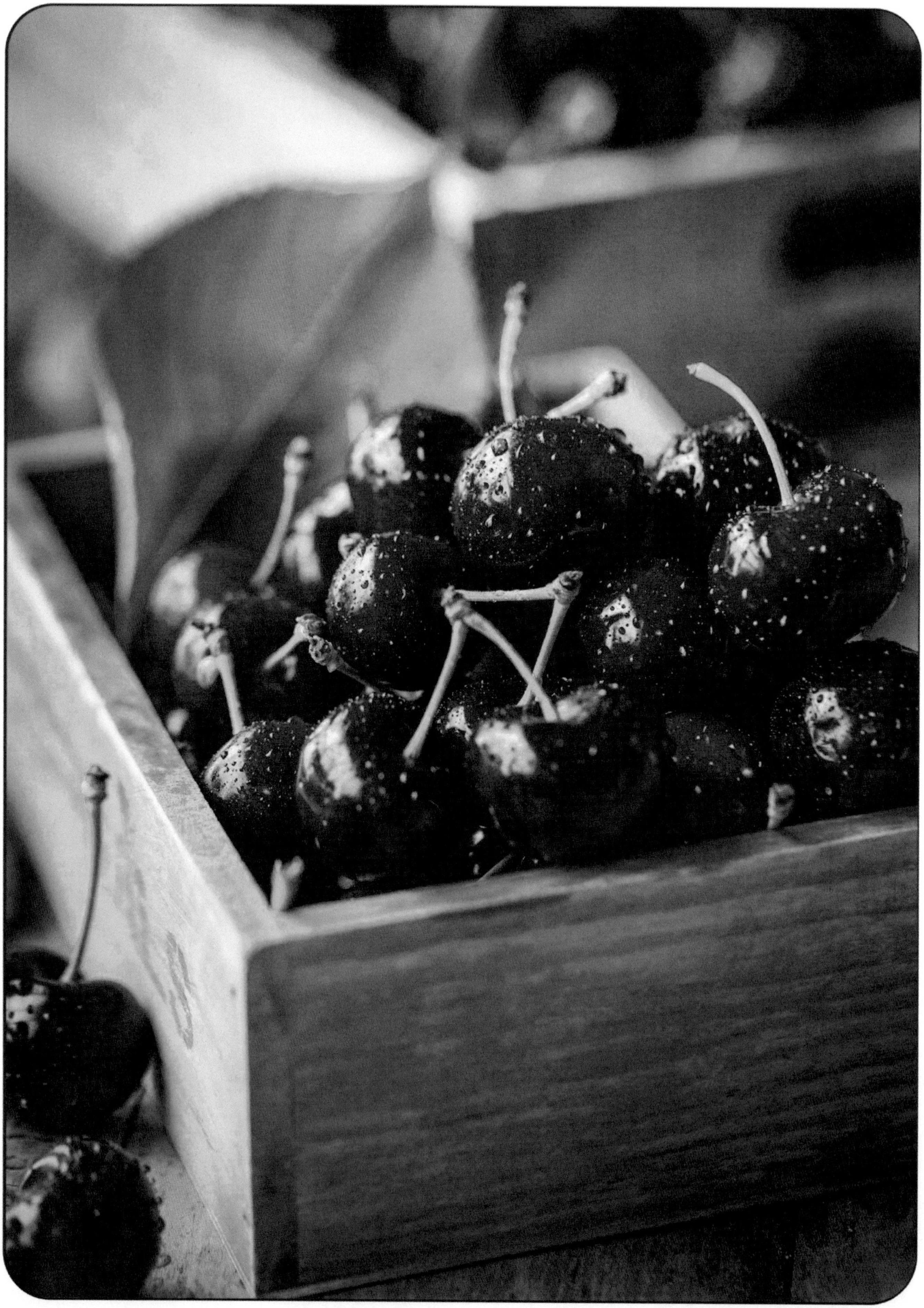

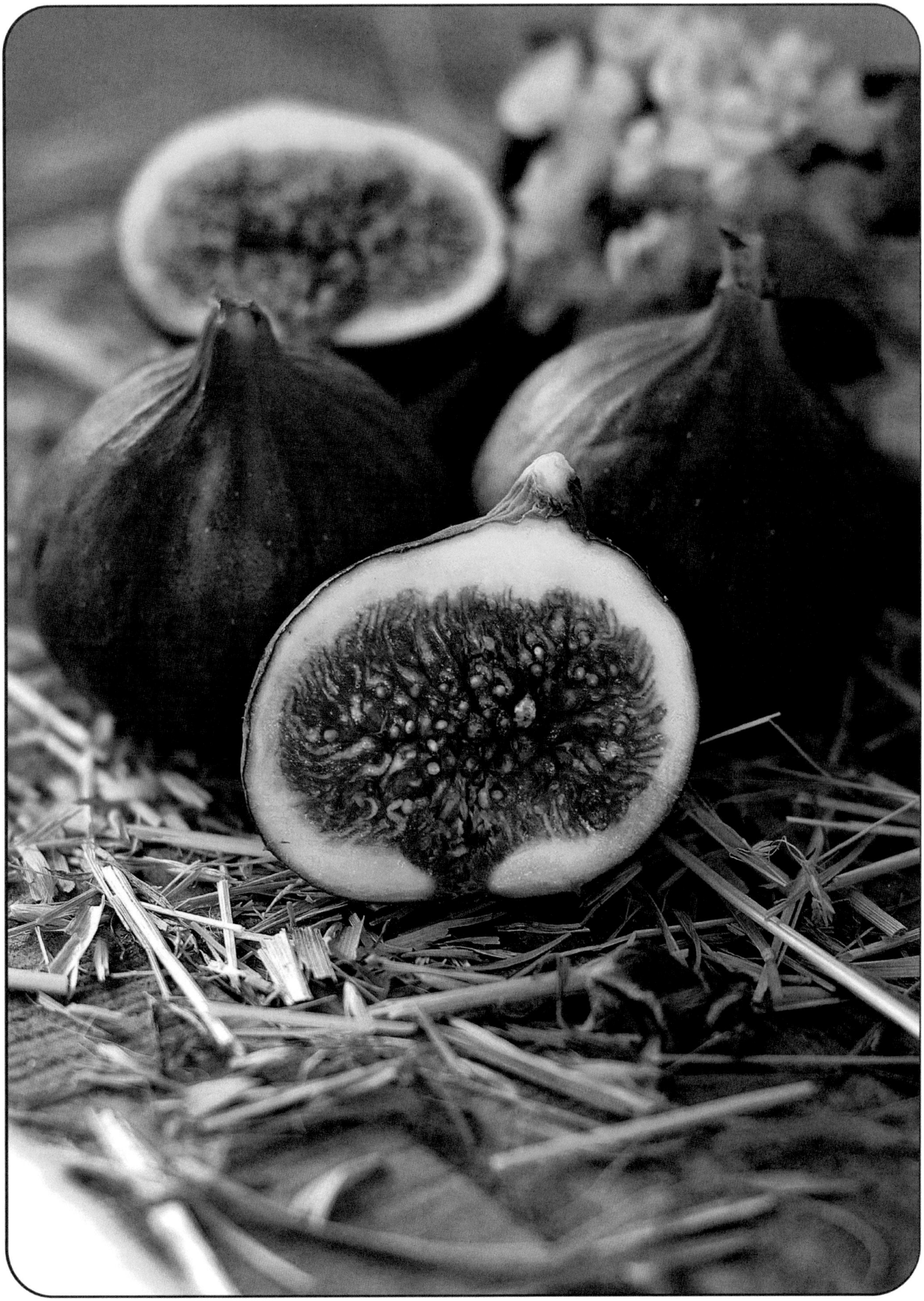

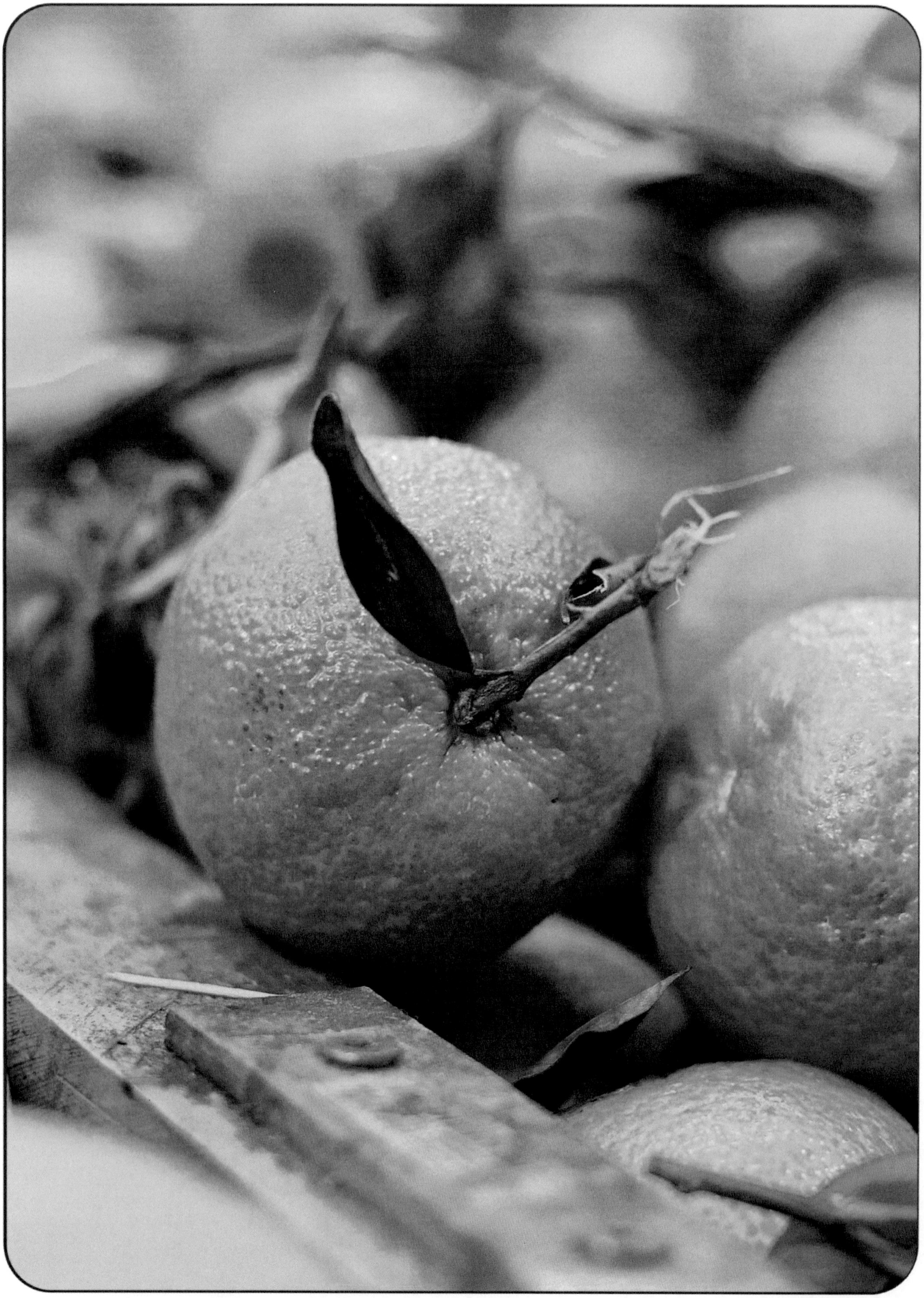

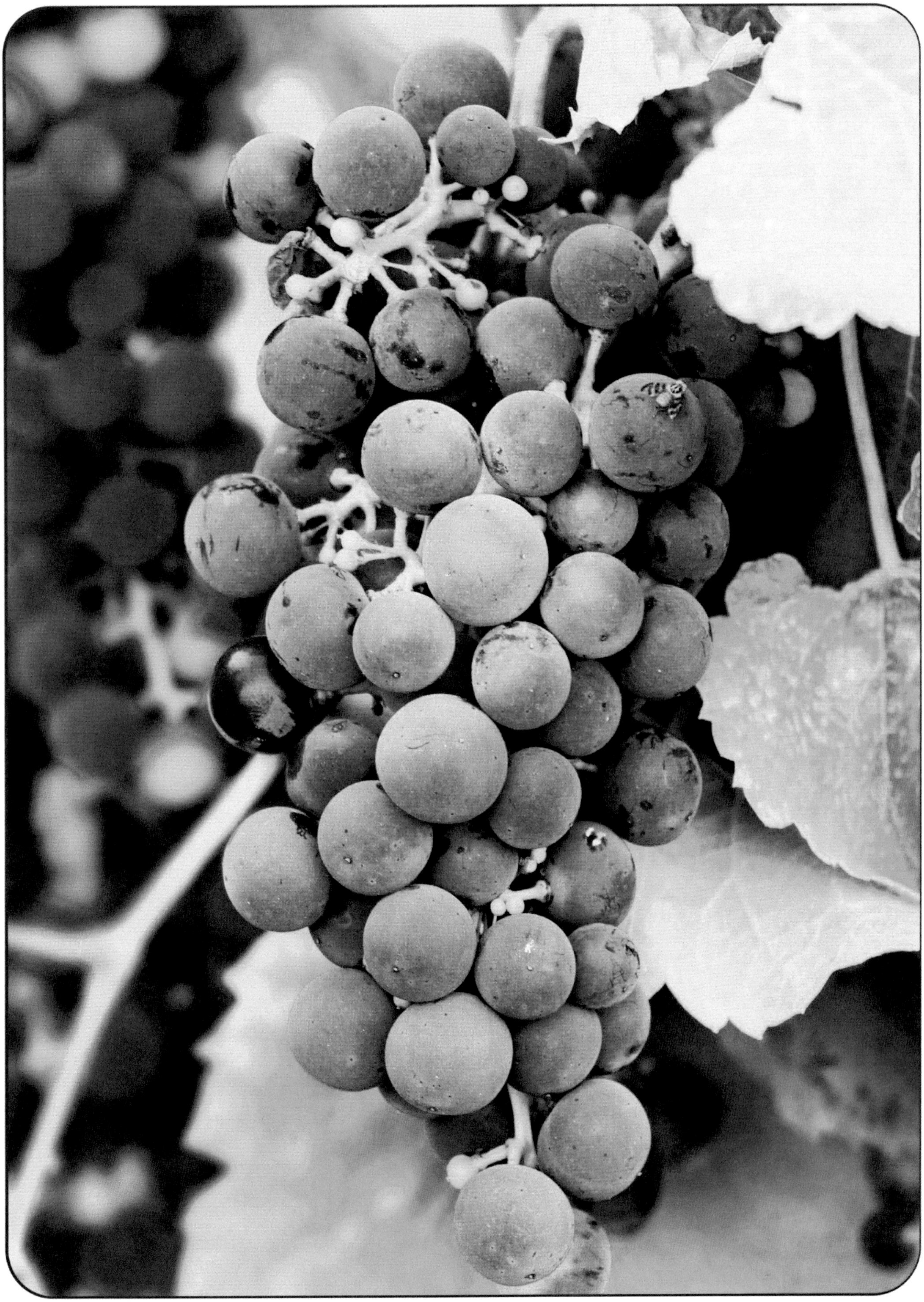

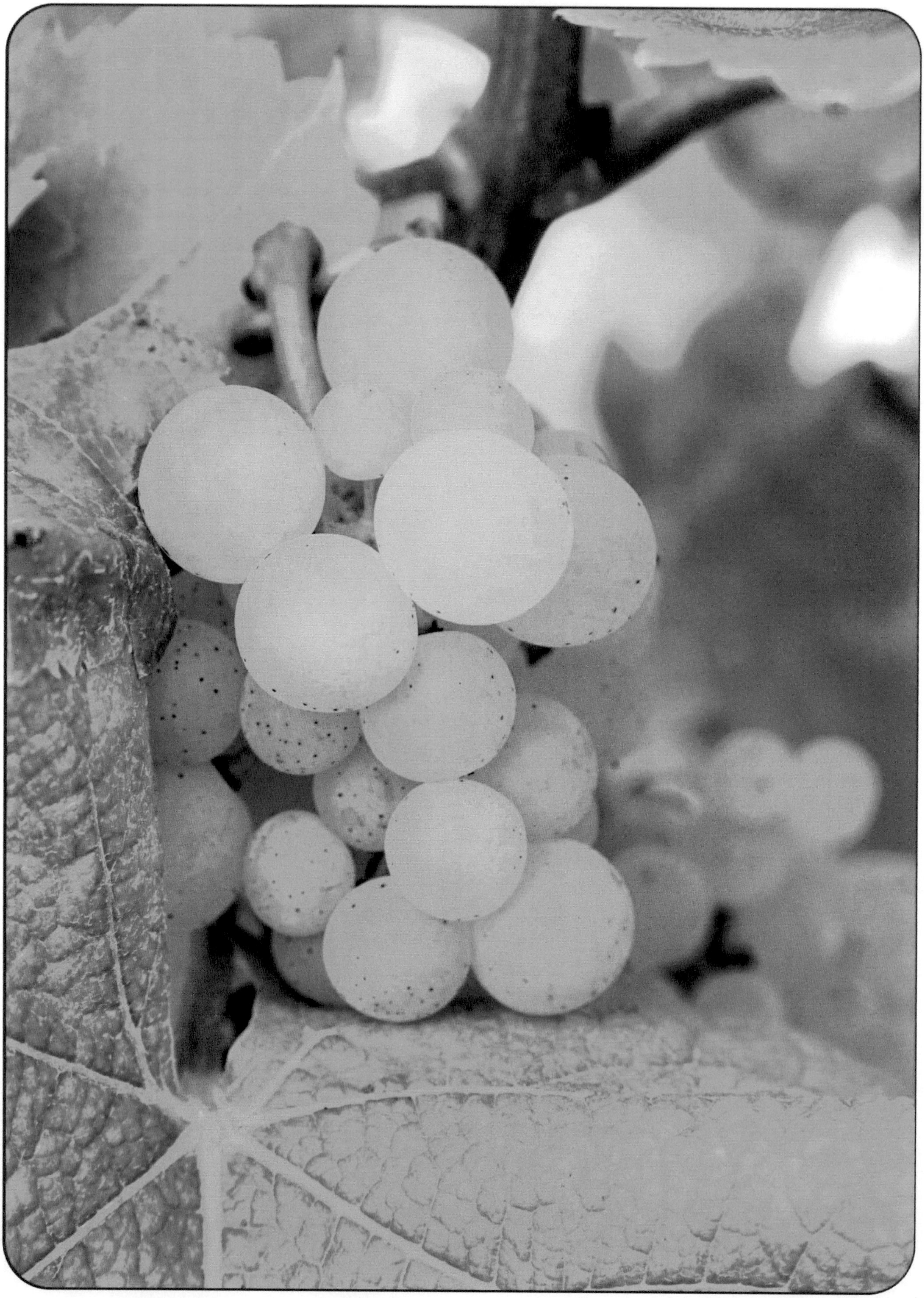

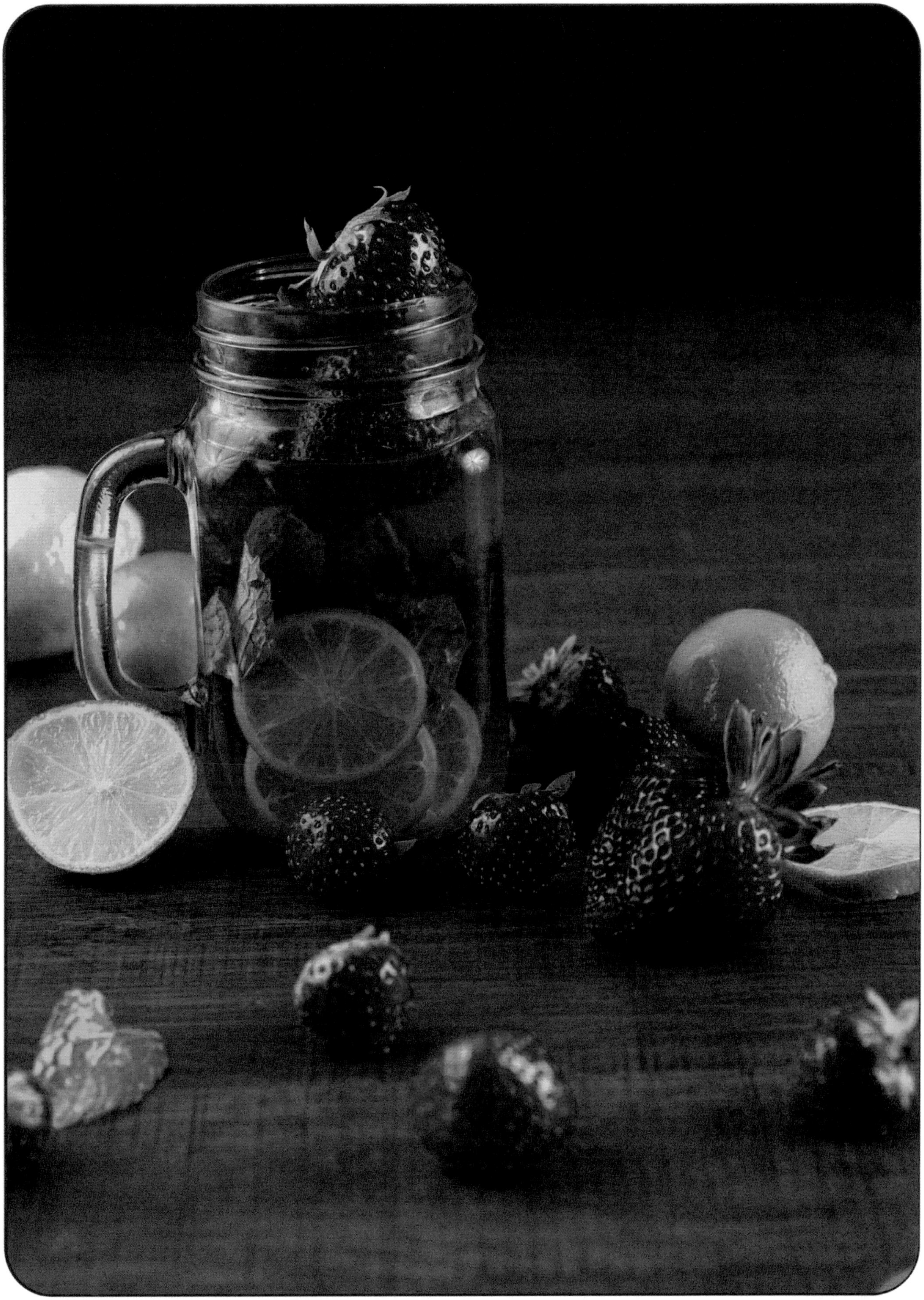

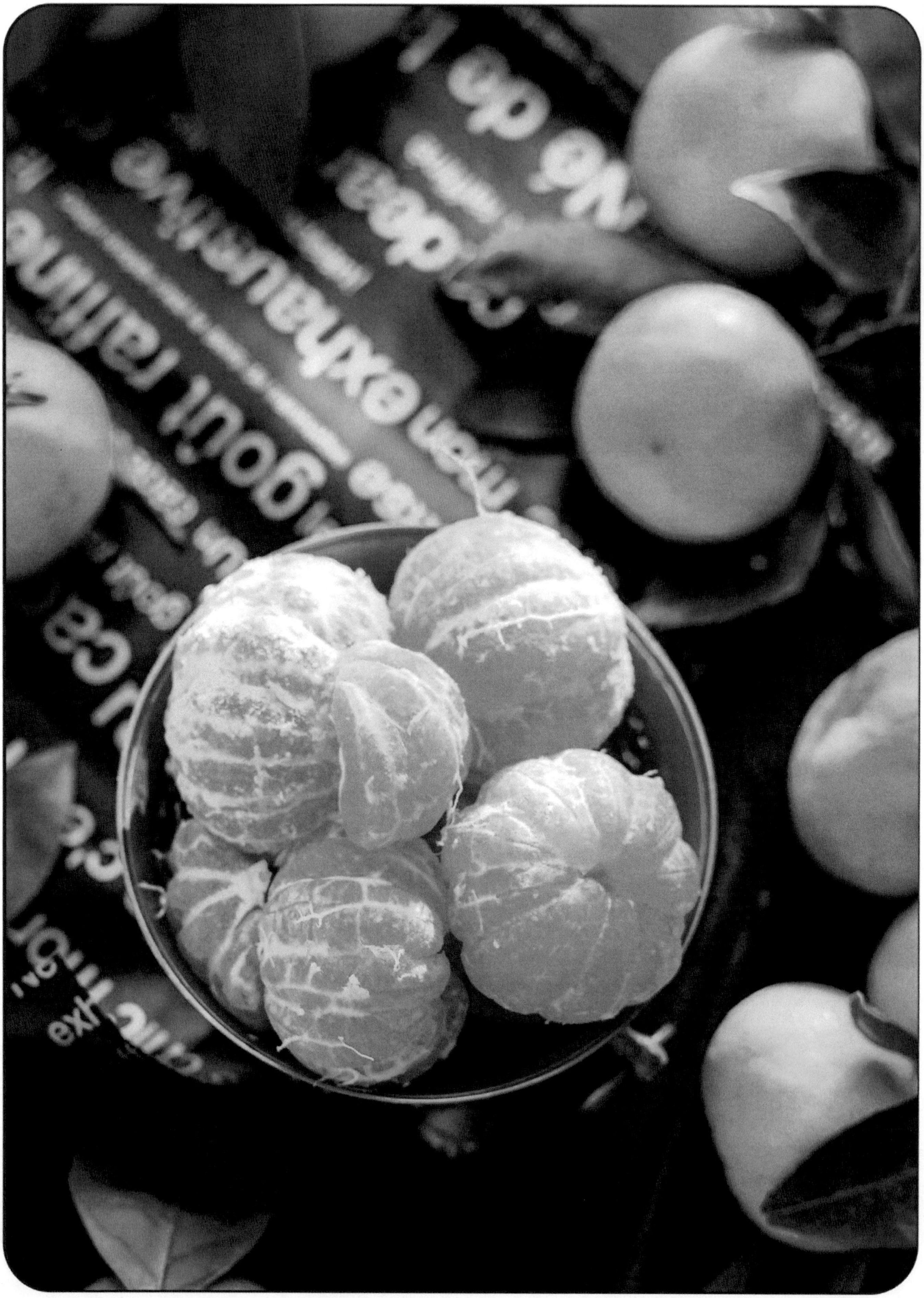

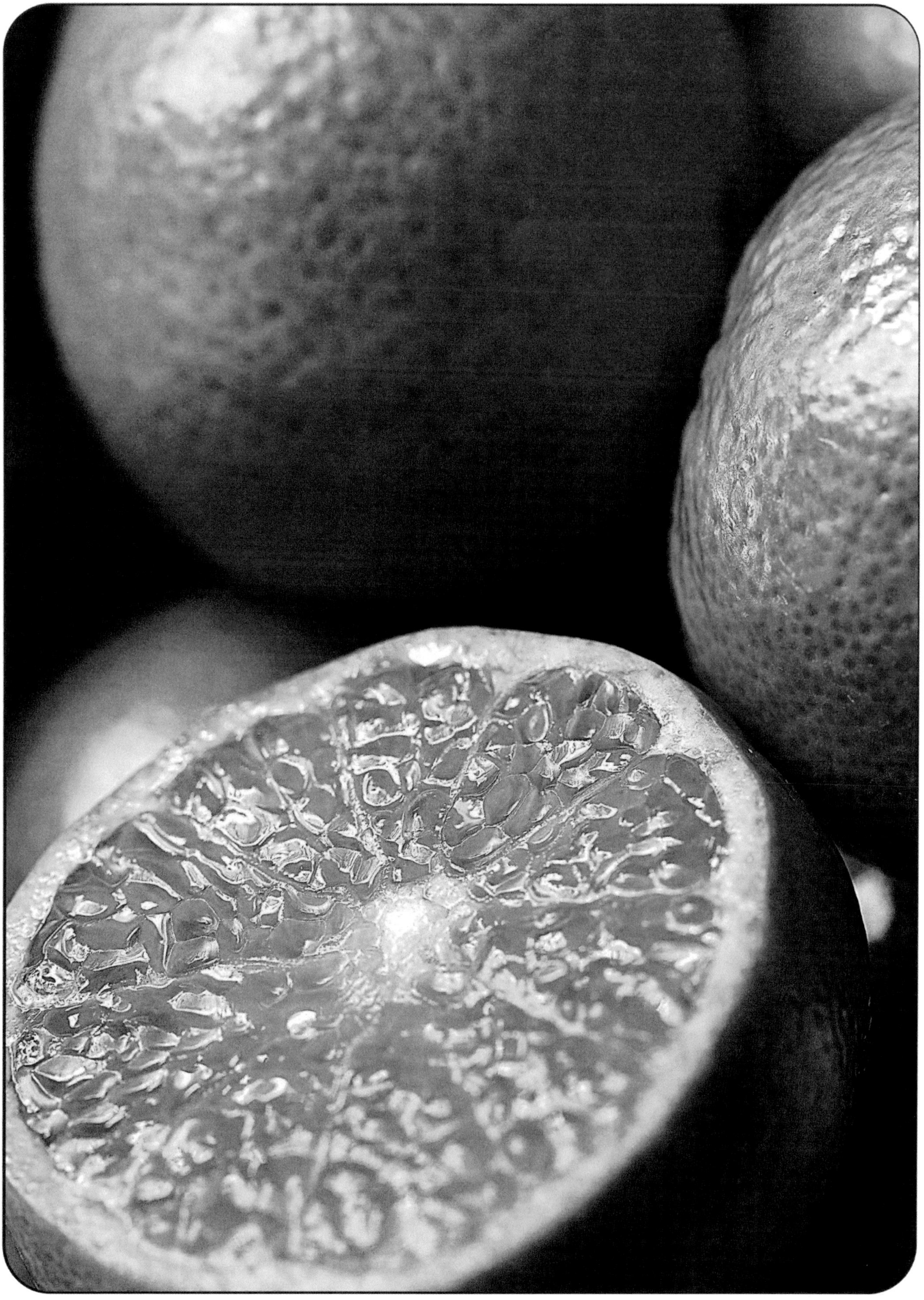

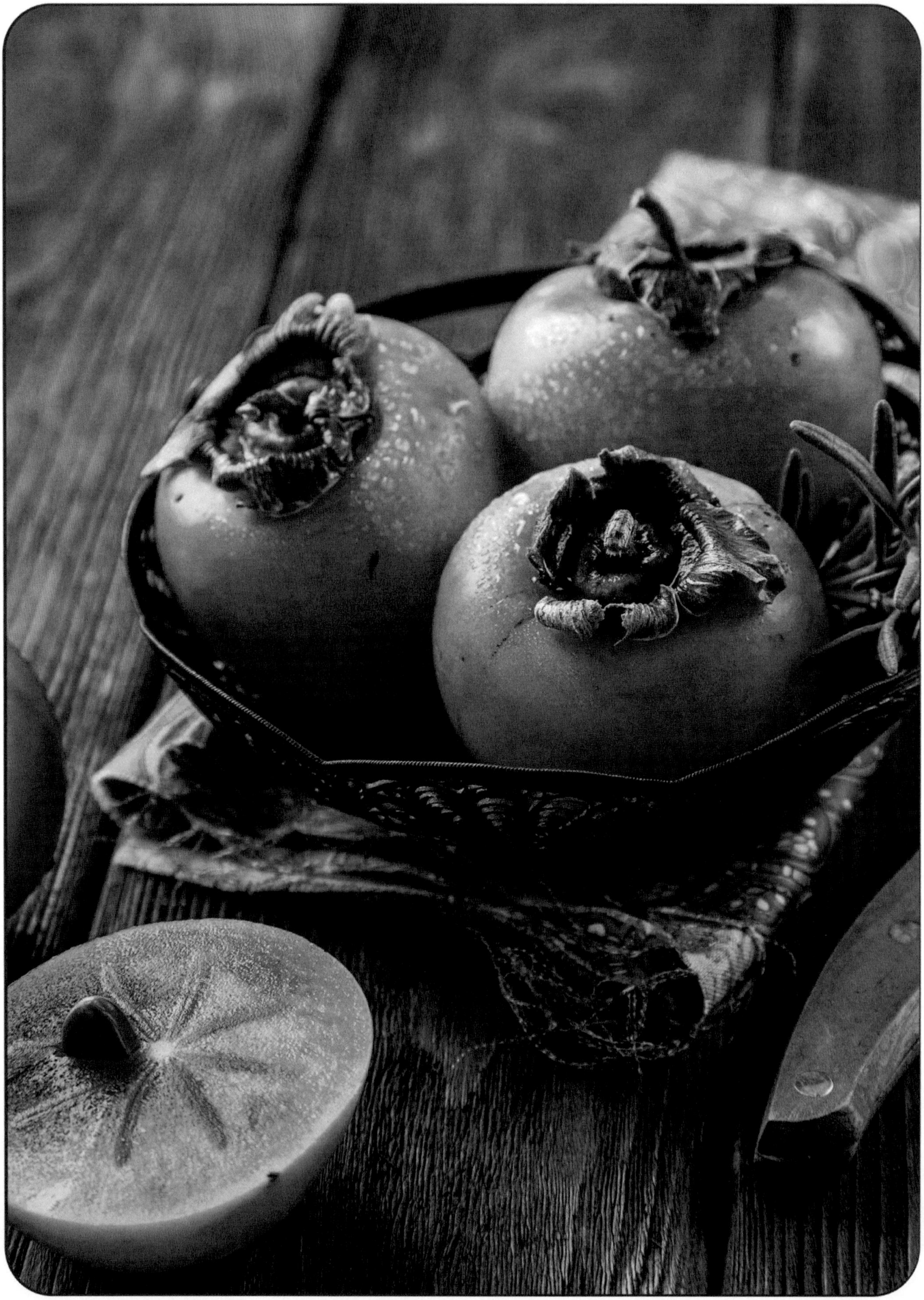

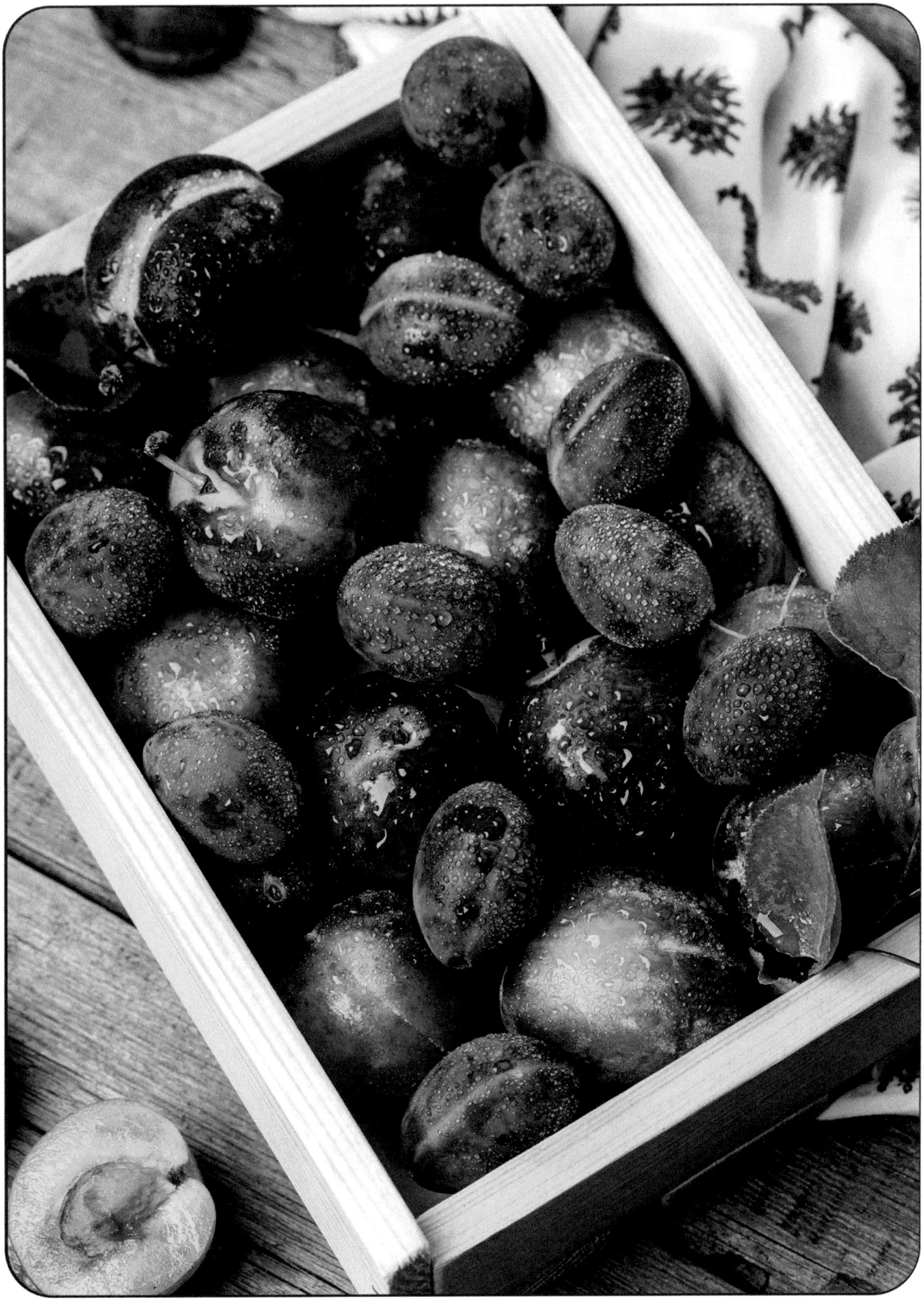

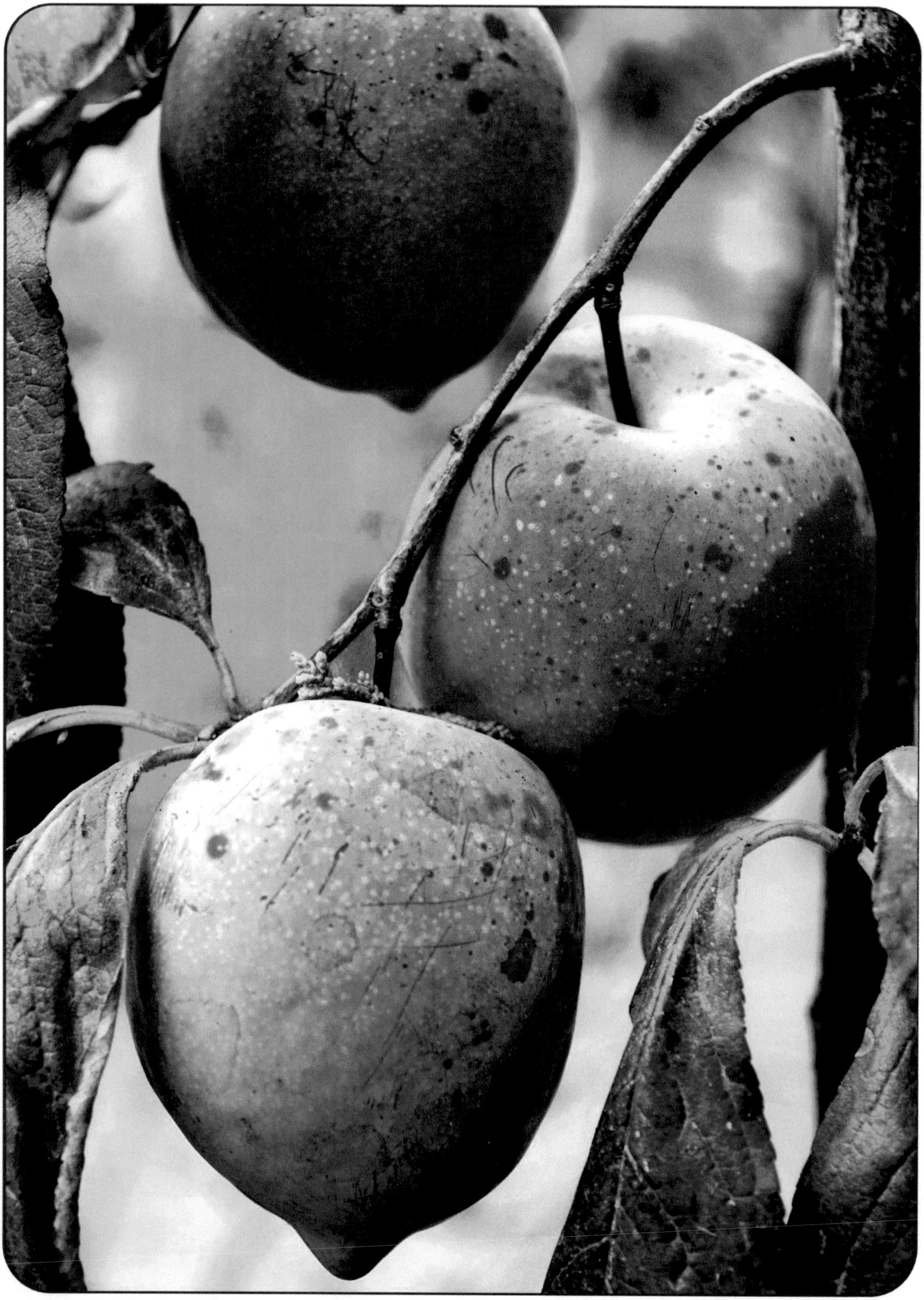

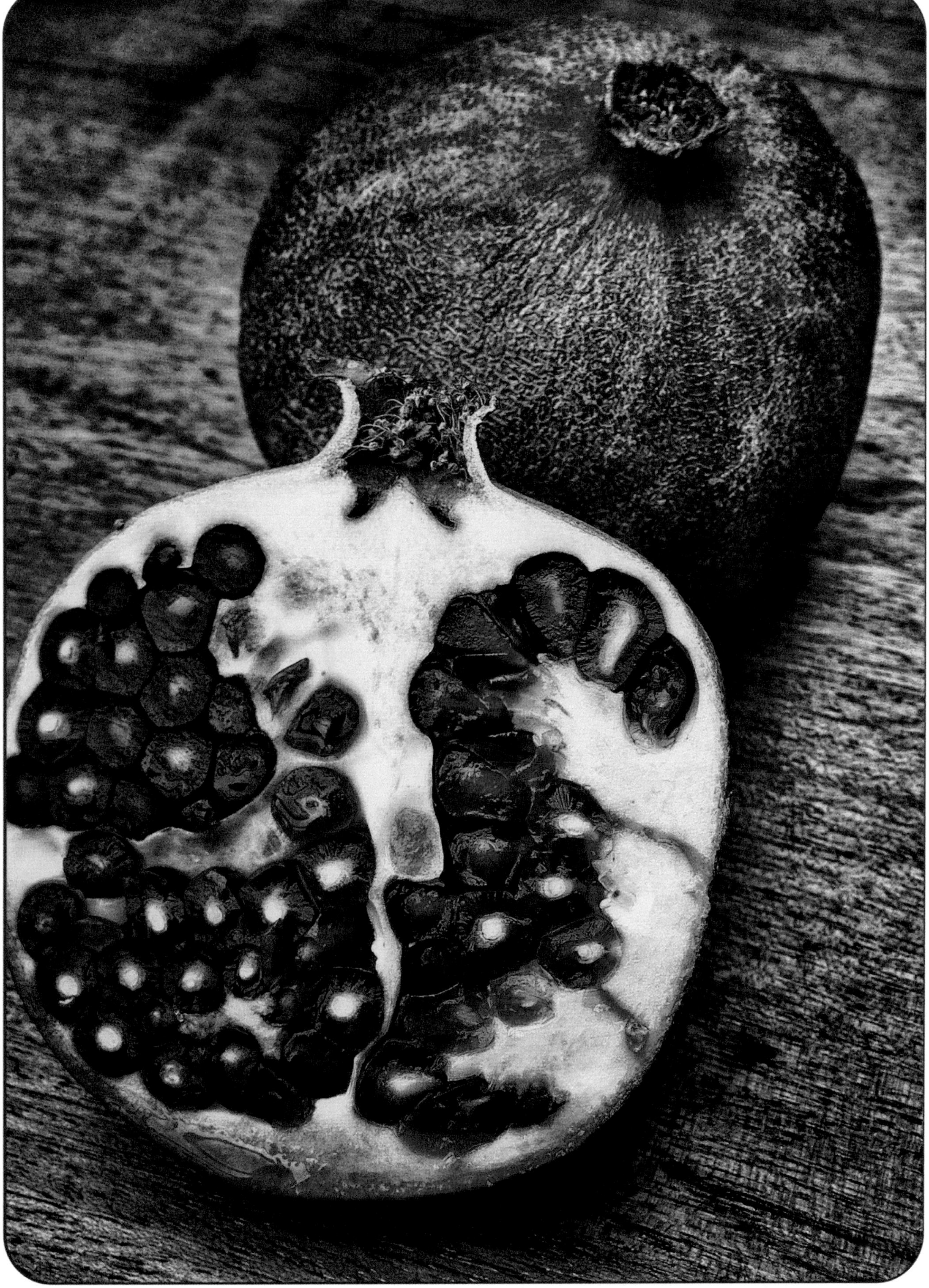

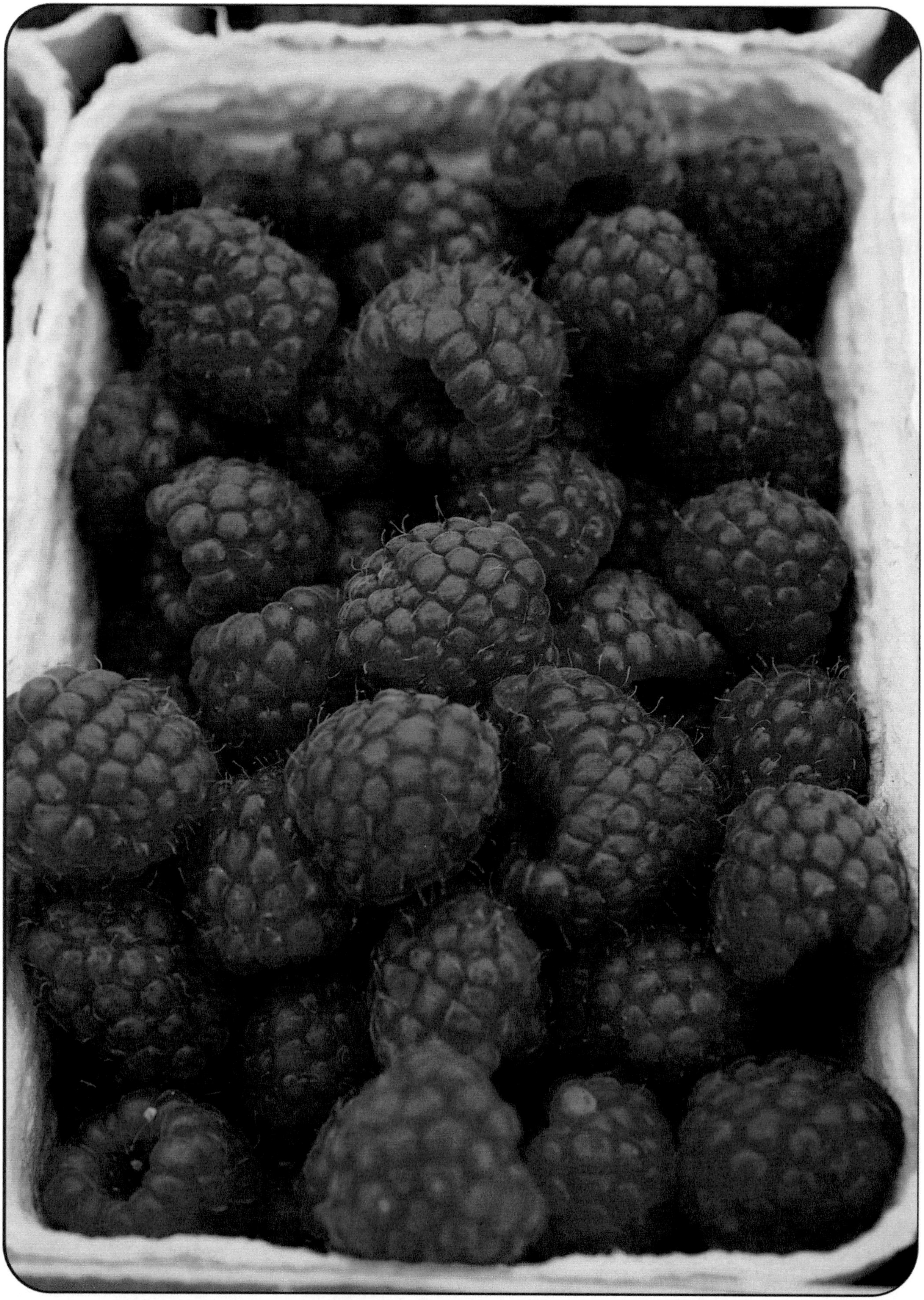

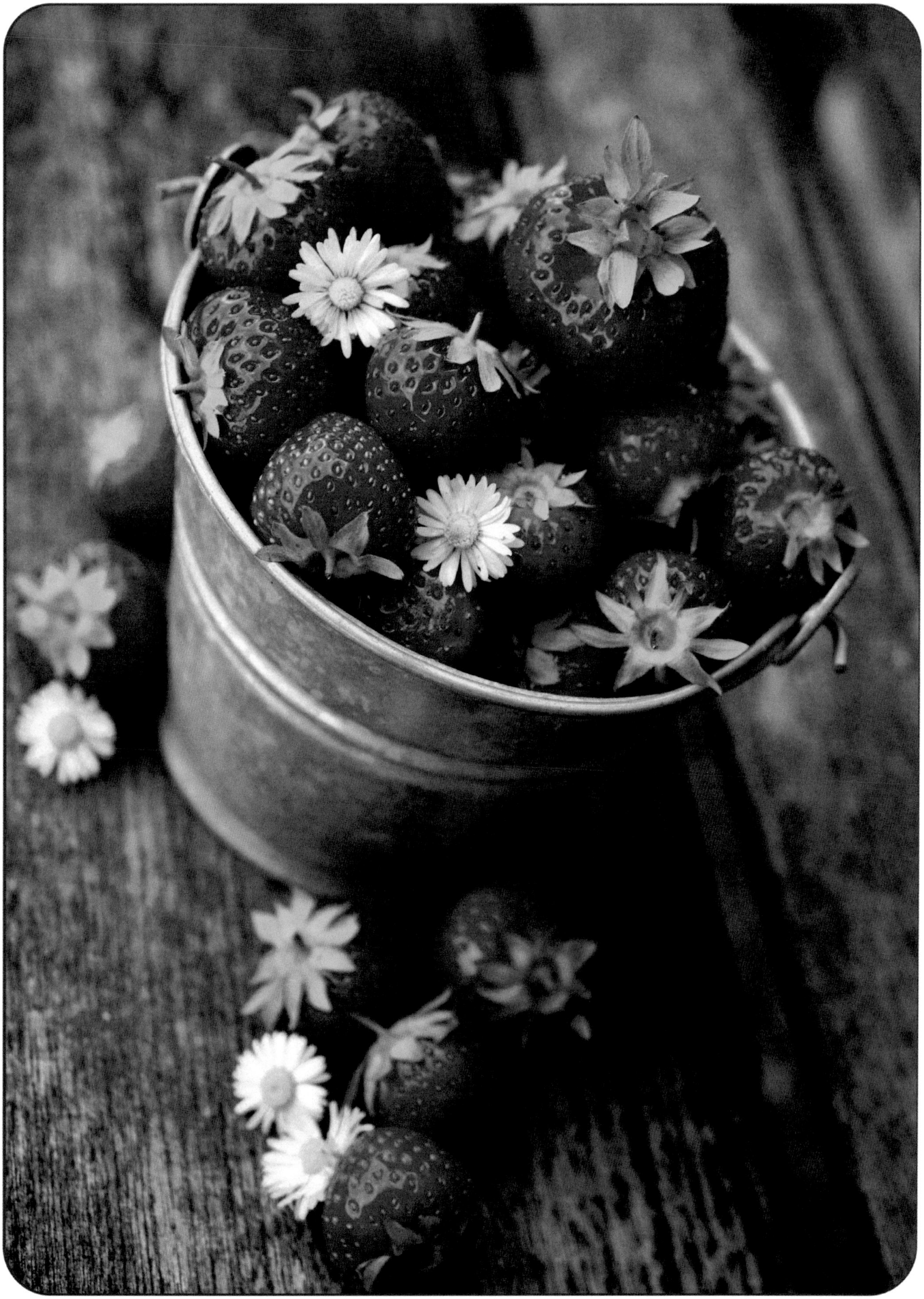

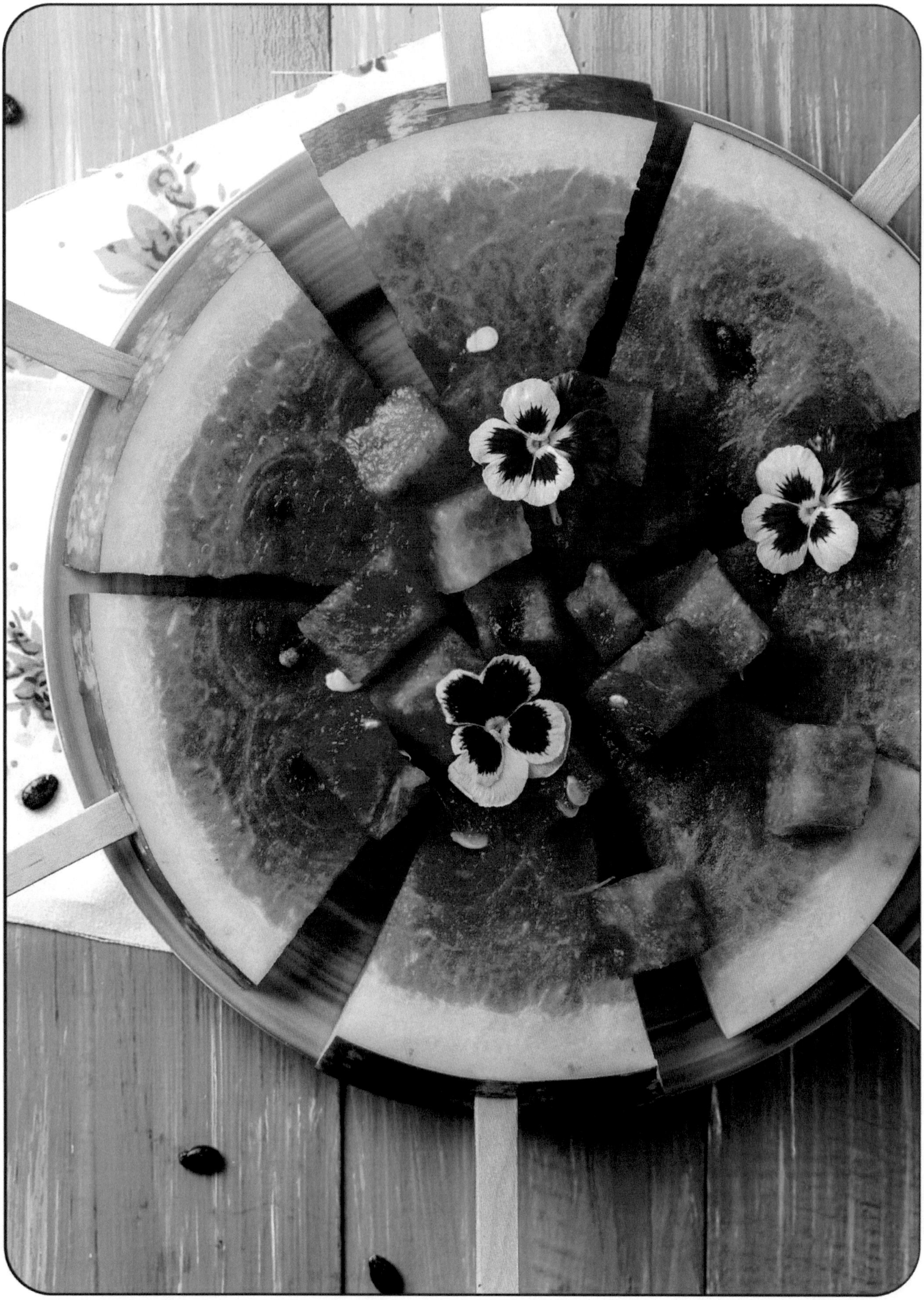

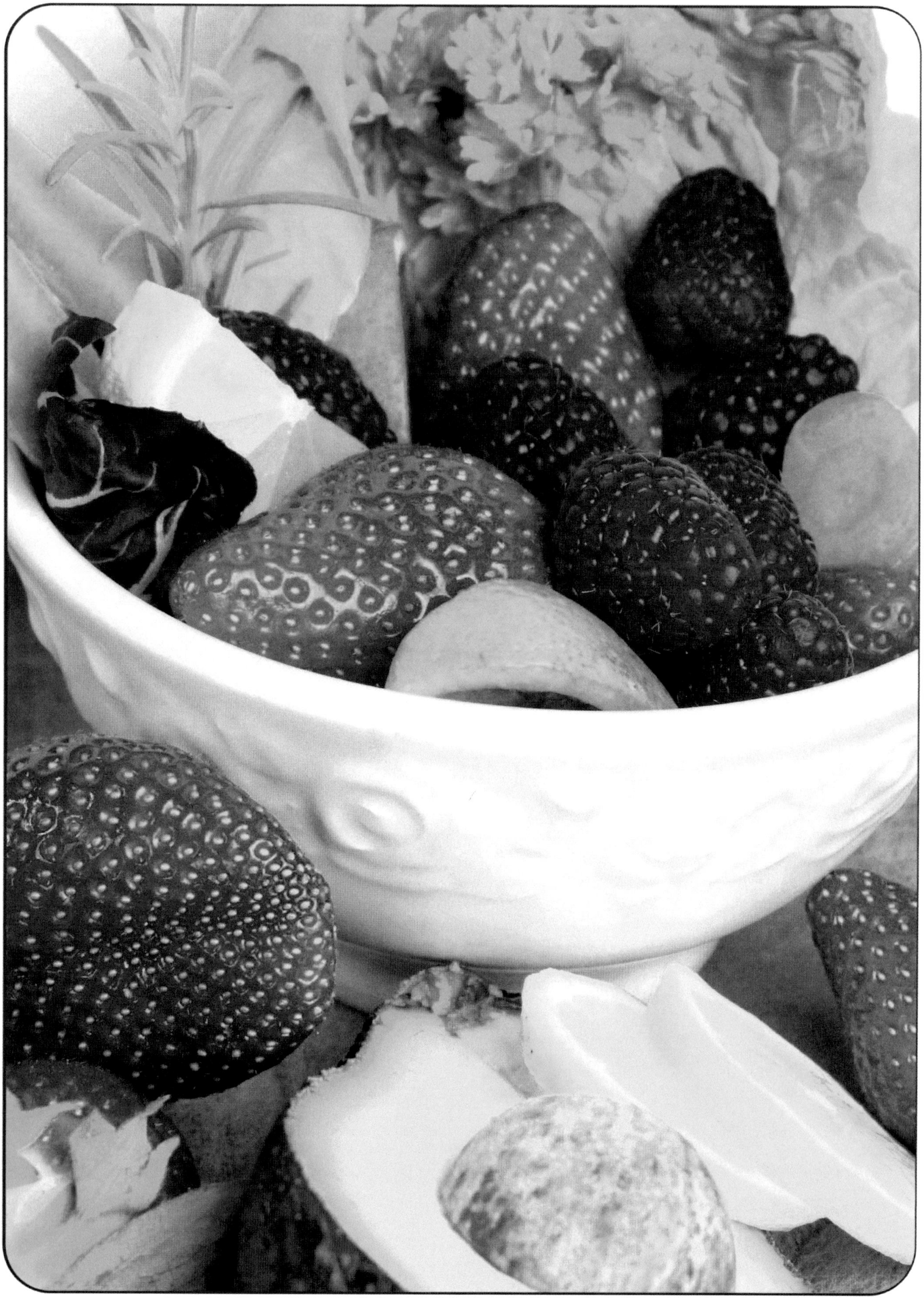

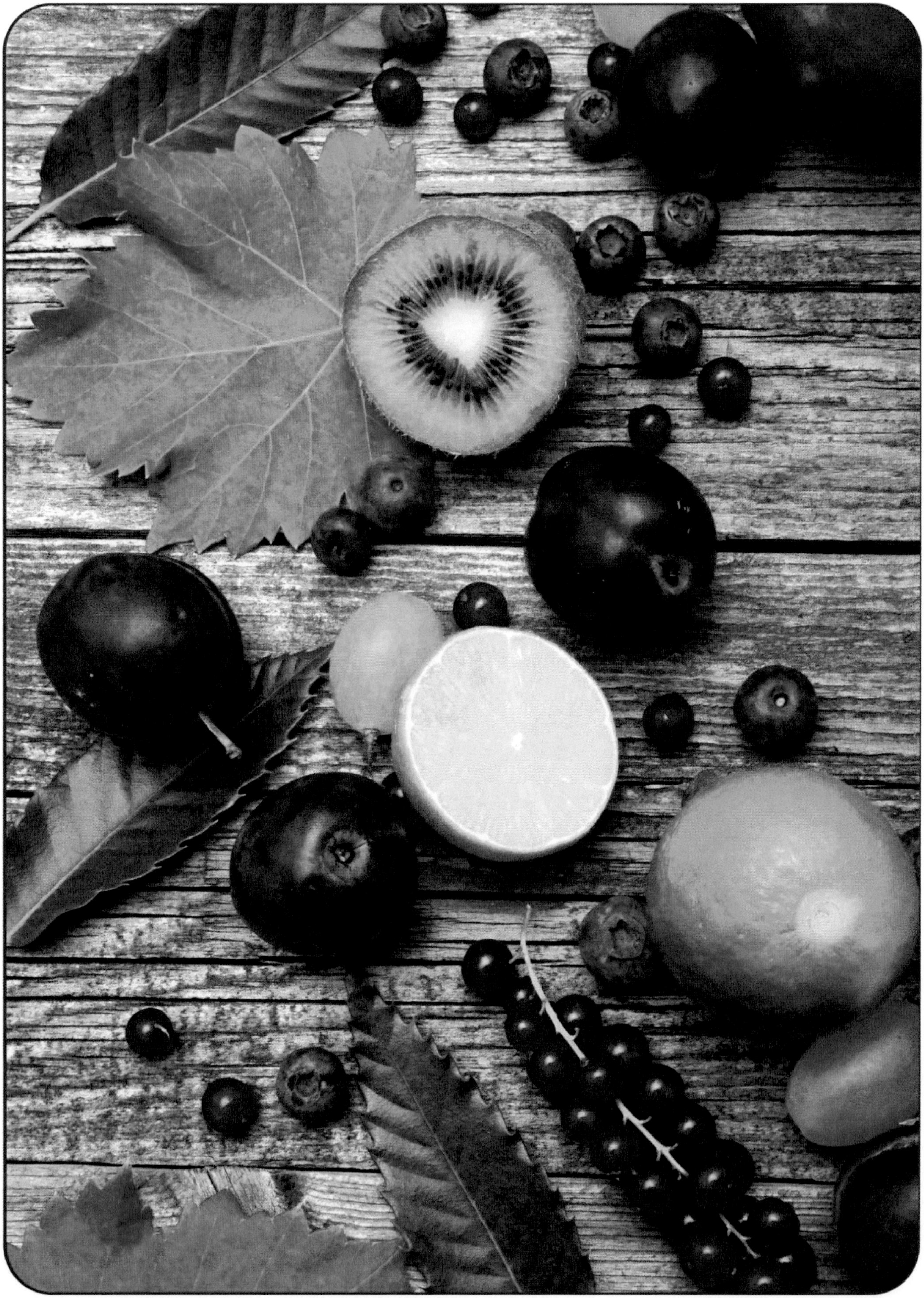

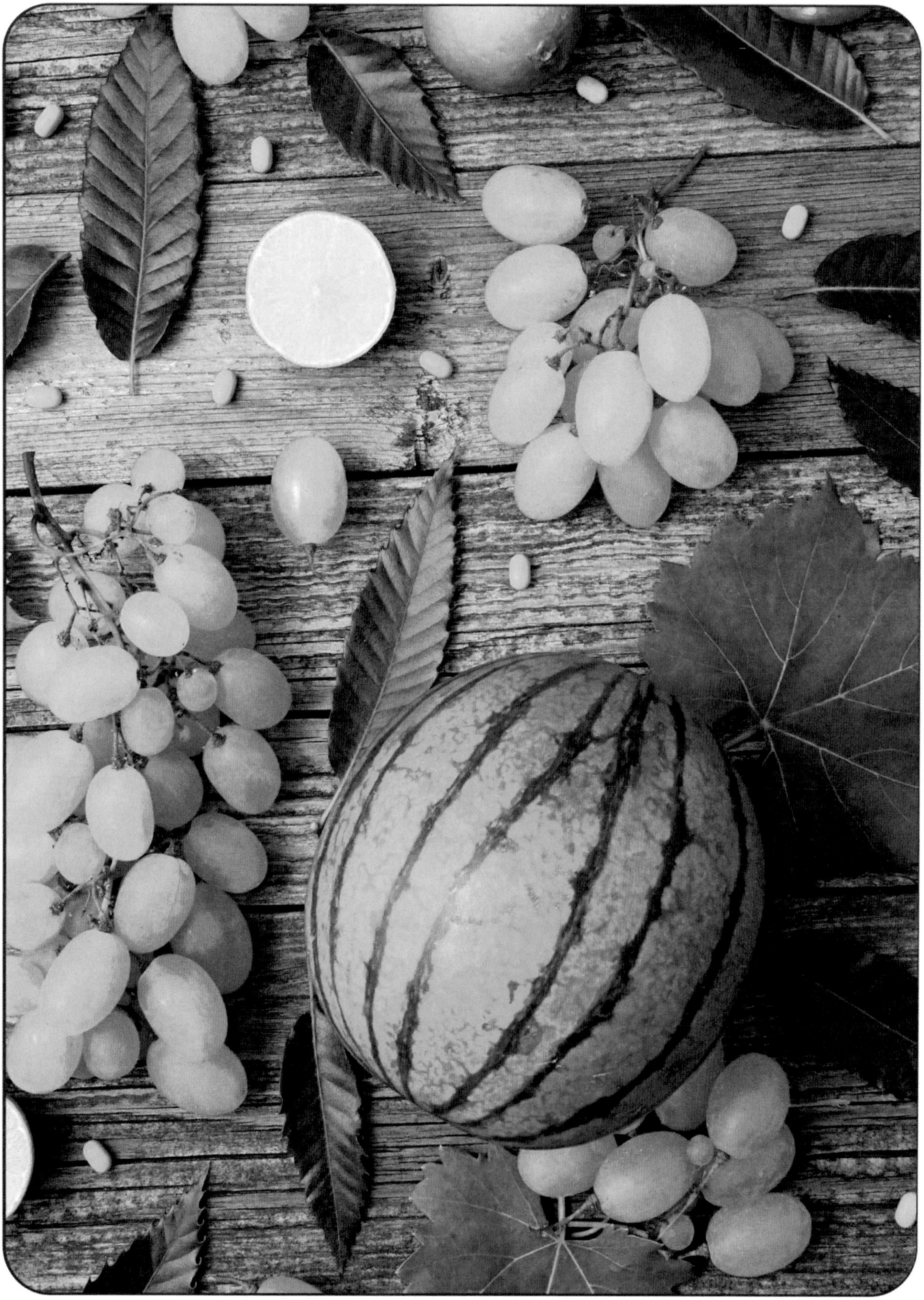

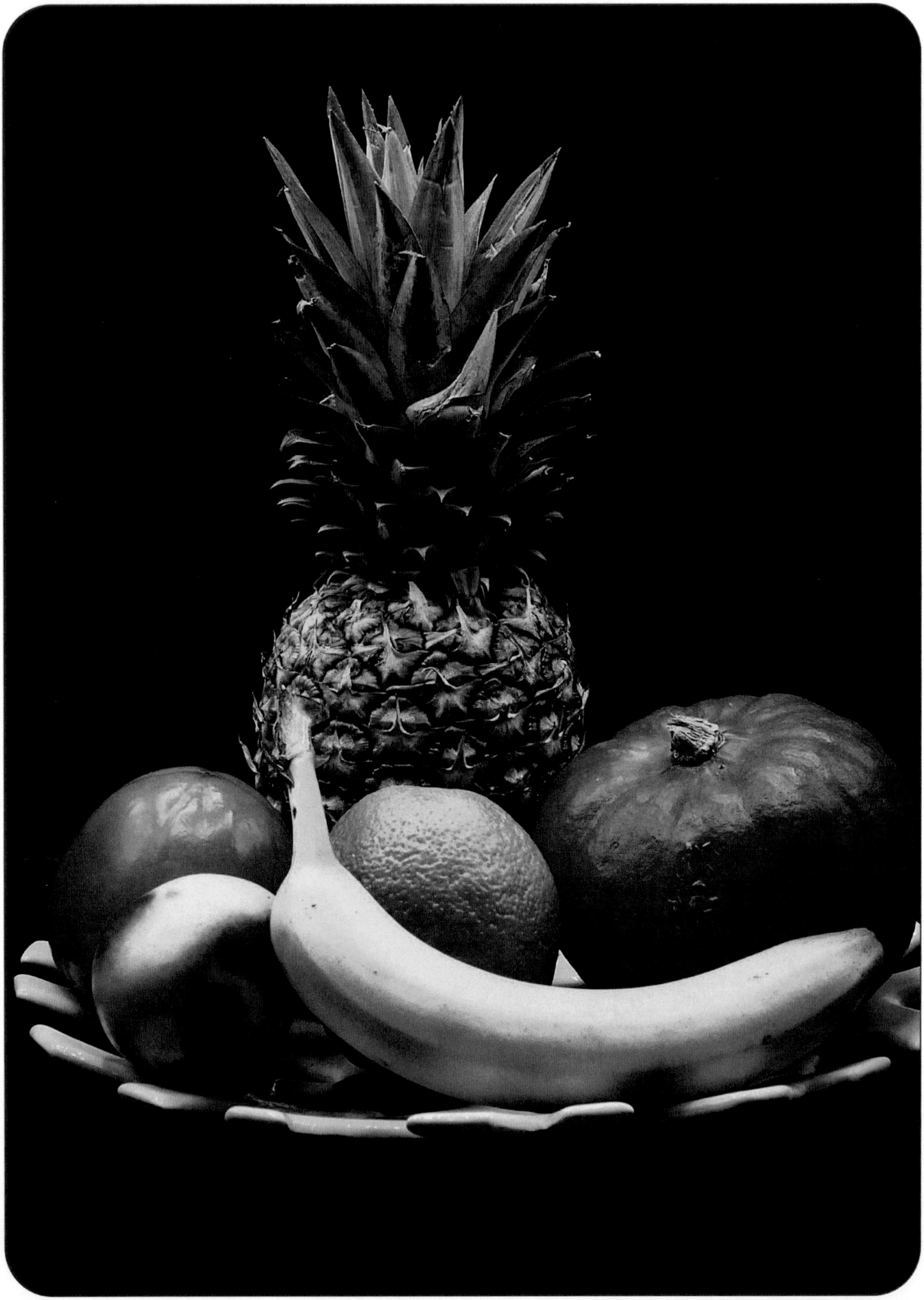

Made in the USA
Las Vegas, NV
14 February 2024

85796987R00026